THE ULTIMATE TEXAS RANGERS TRIVIA BOOK

A Collection of Amazing Trivia Quizzes and Fun Facts for Die-Hard Rangers Fans!

Ray Walker

ISBN: 978-1-953563-95-8

Exclusive Free Book

Crazy Sports Stories

As a thank you for getting a copy of this book I would like to offer you a free copy of my book Crazy Sports Stories which comes packed with interesting stories from your favorite sports such as Football, Hockey, Baseball, Basketball and more.

Grab your free copy over at

RayWalkerMedia.com/Bonus

CONTENTS

INTRODUCTION

The Texas Rangers began in 1961 as the Washington Senators, an expansion franchise. Eleven years later, the team moved to Arlington, Texas, and became the Rangers. It can be hard to stand out in a state that boasts the prowess of the Dallas Cowboys and the Dallas Mavericks, but the Rangers have made their presence known in Texas since 1972.

Although the Texas Rangers have never won a World Series championship, they are often a force to be reckoned with in the American League West. They won the American League Pennant in 2010 and 2011 and have won the American League West Division seven times since 1972.

The Rangers will be moving to a new (air-conditioned!) ballpark in 2020 called Globe Life Field, just across the street from their former ballpark, Globe Life Park, in Arlington. The legends of the players whose numbers the Rangers have retired will carry over to their new home, including Nolan Ryan, Iván "Pudge" Rodriguez, Michael Young, Adrián Beltré, and Johnny Oates, thus highlighting their captivating past.

The thing about baseball is that it is a lot like life. There are good times and bad times, good days and bad days, but you have to do your absolute best to never give up. The Texas Rangers have proven that they refuse to give up.

You don't need a World Series championship to have a storied history filled with both ups and downs. The Texas Rangers have so much interesting history and so many incredible player legacies to be profoundly proud of.

The Rangers are one of two MLB teams in the state of Texas. The Rangers have rivals in the Houston Astros and their American League West counterparts, the Oakland A's, Seattle Mariners, and Los Angeles Angels of Anaheim. Those rivalries make up a lot of their history, as well. From the Lone Star Series to the American League West matchups, you are sure to be entertained if you are a Texas Rangers fan.

CHAPTER 1:

ORIGINS & HISTORY

QUIZ TIME!

1. What were the Texas Rangers known as before they moved to Arlington?

    a. Montreal Expos
    b. Washington Senators
    c. Dallas Cowboys
    d. Dallas Senators

2. In what year did the franchise move to Texas?

    a. 1952
    b. 1962
    c. 1972
    d. 1982

3. The Rangers will move to Globe Life Field in 2020. They have played at Globe Life Park since 1994.

    a. True
    b. False

4. Which division do the Texas Rangers currently play in?

   a. American League West
   b. American League Central
   c. National League West
   d. National League Central

5. What was the name of the stadium that the Rangers played in from 1972 through 1993?

   a. AT&T Stadium
   b. RFK Stadium
   c. Arlington Stadium
   d. Griffith Stadium

6. In 1989, the Texas Rangers were sold to an investment group headed by which former U.S. president?

   a. Barack Obama
   b. Bill Clinton
   c. George H.W. Bush
   d. George W. Bush

7. The Rangers' mascot, named Captain, is what type of animal?

   a. Cow
   b. Bull
   c. Horse
   d. Lizard

8. Who is the longest-tenured manager in Texas Rangers history (as of the end of the 2019 season)?

   a. Ron Washington
   b. Buck Showalter

c. Bobby Valentine
d. A and C

9. What is the name of the Texas Rangers' Triple-A team, and where is it located?

   a. Fresno Grizzlies
   b. Nashville Sounds
   c. Toledo Mud Hens
   d. Columbus Clippers

10. Who was the Rangers' manager when they moved to Arlington and became the Texas Rangers?

   a. Ted Williams
   b. Billy Martin
   c. Don Zimmer
   d. Johnny Oates

11. The Rangers' current general manager, Jon Daniels, was the youngest GM of all time in the MLB at the time of his hiring in 2005 at 28 years old.

   a. True
   b. False

12. Where did the Texas Rangers' name originate?

   a. *Walker Texas Ranger* TV show
   b. An ode to Old West cowboys
   c. The famous law enforcement agency of the same name
   d. The Dallas Cowboys were formerly the Texas Rangers.

13. How many appearances have the Texas Rangers made in the MLB playoffs (as of the end of the 2019 season)?

a. 7
b. 8
c. 9
d. 10

14. What year was the most recent version of the Washington Senators established?

a. 1941
b. 1951
c. 1961
d. 1971

15. That Washington Senators franchise was an expansion team. The Minnesota Twins were the original Washington Senators and hold all of their original records.

a. True
b. False

16. The Washington Senators were a member of which division?

a. American League East
b. National League East
c. American League West
d. National League West

17. Which former Rangers pitcher is now a color commentator on TV for Rangers broadcasts on Fox Sports Southwest?

a. Charlie Hough
b. Kenny Rogers
c. Nolan Ryan
d. C.J. Nitkowski

18. How many World Series did the Washington Senators win?

    a. 0
    b. 1
    c. 2
    d. 3

19. Who was the very first manager of the franchise when it was the Washington Senators?

    a. Eddie Yost
    b. Jim Lemon
    c. Mickey Vernon
    d. Chris Woodward

20. The Rangers franchise has won the most games of any team in the American League West Division all time.

    a. True
    b. False

QUIZ ANSWERS

1. B – Washington Senators
2. C – 1972
3. A – True
4. A – American League West
5. C – Arlington Stadium
6. D – George W. Bush
7. C – Horse
8. D – A and C (Bobby Valentine and Ron Washington each managed the Rangers for 7 years.)
9. B – Nashville Sounds
10. A – Ted Williams
11. A – True
12. C – The famous law enforcement agency of the same name
13. B – 8
14. C – 1961
15. A – True
16. A – American League East
17. D – C.J. Nitkowski
18. A – 0
19. C – Mickey Vernon
20. B – False, Oakland A's hold this record.

DID YOU KNOW?

1. The Texas Rangers franchise has had 27 managers. They are Mickey Vernon, Eddie Yost, Gil Hodges, Jim Lemon, Ted Williams, Whitey Herzog, Del Wilber, Billy Martin, Frank Lucchesi, Eddie Stanky, Connie Ryan, Billy Hunter, Pat Corrales, Don Zimmer, Darrell Johnson, Doug Rader, Bobby Valentine, Toby Harrah, Kevin Kennedy, Johnny Oates, Jerry Narron, Buck Showalter, Ron Washington, Tim Bogar, Jeff Banister, Don Wakamatsu, and Chris Woodward.
2. Team captains for the Rangers have included Buddy Bell (1985), Alex Rodriguez (2004), Michael Young (2004-2012), and Adrián Beltré (2013-2018).
3. Ron Washington is the Texas Rangers' all-time winningest manager with a record of 664-611 (.521).
4. The Washington Senators not only did not win a World Series, they never even made the playoffs.
5. The Washington Senators hosted the 1969 MLB All-Star Game at RFK Stadium. The Texas Rangers hosted the 1995 MLB All-Star Game at Globe Life Park. MLB Commissioner Rob Manfred has told fans to expect an MLB All-Star Game to be held at the new Globe Life Field at some point in the near future but has not yet specified a year.

6. Former Rangers players inducted into the National Baseball Hall of Fame include Fergie Jenkins, Gaylord Perry, Iván "Pudge" Rodriguez, and, of course, Nolan Ryan.
7. The Rangers' first game in Arlington was postponed by a players' strike. Their inaugural game finally took place against the California Angels nine days later. The Rangers lost that game to the Angels, 1-0.
8. The official groundbreaking ceremony for Globe Life Park took place on October 30, 1991. The official groundbreaking for Globe Life Field took place in September 2017. The distance from home plate to the right-field foul pole at Globe Life Field is 326 feet to honor former Rangers manager, Johnny Oates. Oates wore number 26 when he managed the Rangers.
9. The Texas Rangers franchise first made the MLB playoffs in 1996. This was the first season they won the American League West. The Rangers played the New York Yankees in the American League Division Series (ALDS) but could not make it past New York. The Yankees went on to win the World Series that year.
10. The Rangers play most of their weekend games at night between May and September due to hot temperatures that average around 100 degrees. This may change, however, in the coming seasons because Globe Life Field will be equipped with a roof and air conditioning.

CHAPTER 2:

JERSEYS & NUMBERS

QUIZ TIME!

1. In 1983, the Rangers added a logo to the front of their jerseys in the shape of the state of Texas with a large baseball and the letters "T.R." on top.
   a. True
   b. False
2. Which number has NOT been retired by the Texas Rangers (as of the end of the 2019 season)?
   a. 7
   b. 10
   c. 22
   d. 29
3. The Washington Senators' colors were purple and gold.
   a. True
   b. False
4. What uniform number does shortstop Elvis Andrus wear for the Rangers?

a. 4
b. 3
c. 2
d. 1

5. What uniform number did Nolan Ryan wear with the Rangers?

a. 30
b. 32
c. 34
d. 37

6. Who is the latest player to have his number retired by the Rangers (as of the 2019 season)?

a. Iván Rodriguez
b. Adrián Beltré
c. Michael Young
d. Nolan Ryan

7. No Rangers player has ever worn the uniform number 0.

a. True
b. False

8. Who is the only Rangers player to ever wear number 84?

a. Prince Fielder
b. Rougned Odor
c. Armando Galarraga
d. Craig Gentry

9. Which former Rangers legend had his number 7 retired by the team?

a. Nolan Ryan
b. Adrián Beltré
c. Michael Young
d. Iván Rodriguez

10. Players' numbers first appeared on the front of Rangers jerseys in 1984.

    a. True
    b. False

11. What are the Texas Rangers' official team colors?

    a. Blue and red
    b. Blue, red, and black
    c. Blue, red, and metallic gold
    d. Blue, red, and white

12. Johnny Oates was the Rangers' manager for seven seasons. His number ____ was retired by the team in 2005, soon after he passed away on Christmas Eve 2004.

    a. 23
    b. 24
    c. 25
    d. 26

13. The Rangers debuted powder blue alternate uniforms featuring a script "Rangers" across the front, which was last used in 1993. The Rangers last wore powder blue uniforms from 1975 through 1982.

    a. True
    b. False

14. What jersey number did R.A. Dickey wear as a Ranger?

    a. 40
    b. 43
    c. 45
    d. 47

15. What jersey number did Mark Teixeira wear as a Ranger?

    a. 23
    b. 22
    c. 21
    d. 19

16. What jersey number did Juan Gonzalez wear as a Ranger?

    a. 16
    b. 19
    c. 14
    d. 12

17. Joey Gallo currently (as of the 2019 season) wears the number ____ for the Rangers.

    a. 10
    b. 11
    c. 12
    d. 13

18. What jersey number did Alex Rodriguez wear as a Ranger?

    a. 3
    b. 13
    c. 30
    d. 33

19. What jersey number did pitcher Yu Darvish wear as a Ranger?

    a. 10
    b. 11
    c. 12
    d. 13

20. What number did second baseman Ian Kinsler wear during his tenure with the Rangers?

    a. 50
    b. 25
    c. 15
    d. 5

QUIZ ANSWERS

1. A – True
2. C – 22
3. B – False
4. D – 1
5. C – 34
6. C – Michael Young
7. B – False, Al Oliver, Oddibe McDowell, and Junior Ortiz have.
8. A – Prince Fielder
9. D – Iván Rodriguez
10. A – True
11. D – Blue, red, and white
12. D – 26
13. A – True
14. C – 45
15. A – 23
16. B – 19
17. D – 13
18. A – 3
19. B – 11
20. D – 5

DID YOU KNOW?

1. The Texas Rangers' mascot has multiple uniforms to match whatever the team is wearing for that game.
2. The Rangers have retired Iván "Pudge" Rodriguez's number 7, Michael Young's number 10, Johnny Oates' number 26, Adrián Beltré's number 29, Nolan Ryan's number 44, and, of course, Jackie Robinson's number 42.
3. In 1996, the Rangers added a patch on the left sleeve of their jerseys of a diamond with a Texas star in the middle to represent their Lone Star State.
4. Nolan Ryan was the first player to be inducted into the National Baseball Hall of Fame wearing a Rangers hat on his commemorative plaque.
5. Rafael Palmeiro wore both number 3 and number 25 during his stints with the Rangers.
6. Fergie Jenkins wore both number 19 and number 31 as a Ranger.
7. Josh Hamilton wore number 32 when he was with the Rangers.
8. Cole Hamels wore number 35 with the Rangers, as well as with the Phillies and Cubs.
9. Kenny Rogers wore number 37 during each of his stints with the Rangers.

10. In 2019, the Rangers wore a patch on their sleeves that read "Final Season" as their farewell to Globe Life Park.

CHAPTER 3:

FAMOUS QUOTES

QUIZ TIME!

1. Former Rangers manager Ron Washington was portrayed in a baseball movie, and his character uttered the famous line, "It's incredibly hard." Which movie is this quote from?

    a. *Trouble with the Curve*
    b. *Million Dollar Arm*
    c. *Moneyball*
    d. *Fever Pitch*

2. Which former Rangers player said, "I don't think about how many people are watching me. I'm just happy to play baseball for myself."?

    a. Rafael Palmeiro
    b. Vladimir Guerrero
    c. Iván Rodriguez
    d. Nelson Cruz

3. Which former Rangers manager was quoted as saying,

"What is it about our sports world, and our society in general, that wants to know about something before it happens? I'm ok knowing about it when it happens."?

a. Ron Washington
b. Bobby Valentine
c. Johnny Oates
d. Buck Showalter

4. Which former Ranger once said, "Discover your uniqueness; then discipline yourself to develop it."?

   a. Nolan Ryan
   b. Jim Sundberg
   c. R.A. Dickey
   d. Iván Rodriguez

5. Which former Rangers player is quoted as saying, "I don't play it for the money. I play it because I love the game."?

   a. Josh Hamilton
   b. Jose Canseco
   c. Harold Baines
   d. Iván Rodriguez

6. Which former Ranger said, "Enjoying success requires the ability to adapt. Only by being open to change will you have a true opportunity to get the most from your talent."?

   a. Jeff Burroughs
   b. Kenny Rogers
   c. Nolan Ryan
   d. Bert Campaneris

7. Which former Ranger is quoted as saying, "You have to look yourself in the mirror and see what you can do to help the ballclub. It doesn't matter what happened yesterday if you're losing 20 in a row. The next game is the one you're going to win and believe you're going to win."?
   a. Michael Young
   b. Adrián Beltré
   c. Nelson Cruz
   d. Gerald Laird
8. Former Rangers pitcher Charlie Hough once said, "A life is not important except in the impact it has on other lives."
   a. True
   b. False
9. Which former Ranger is quoted as saying, "I believe a champion wins in his mind first, then plays the game, not the other way around."?
   a. Iván Rodriguez
   b. Nolan Ryan
   c. Alex Rodriguez
   d. Ian Kinsler
10. Which former Ranger said, "I always thought that there was going to be life after baseball, and so I designed that in my life I would have other interests after baseball that I would be able to step into. And I didn't realize the grip that baseball had on me and on my family."?
    a. Nolan Ryan
    b. Michael Young

c. Johnny Oates
d. Iván Rodriguez

11. Which former Ranger once said of Alex Rodriguez: "They got the best player in the world to play shortstop... I want to play with that guy. I crossed my fingers for the rest of the winter that they wouldn't trade me."?

    a. Rafael Palmeiro
    b. Michael Young
    c. Mark Teixeira
    d. Mike Lamb

12. Which former Ranger is quoted as saying, "I'm half Italian and my name is Portuguese. Michael Young is half Mexican. There are players from the United States that have heritage elsewhere and it's a great thing to have a World Cup to celebrate the whole world. It shows the world that baseball is important and how great the game is."?

    a. Mark Teixeira
    b. Rafael Palmeiro
    c. Vladimir Guerrero
    d. Bartolo Colón

13. Which Ranger was former Toronto Blue Jay Jose Bautista referring to when he said, "He got me pretty good so I have to give him that. But it takes a little bit of a bigger man to knock me down," after their on-field fight?

    a. Elvis Andrus
    b. Robinson Chirinos

c. Rougned Odor
d. Jurickson Profar

14. Which former Rangers pitcher is quoted as saying, "You feel like a rock star in some ways," when talking about being the Opening Day starter?

    a. Mike Minor
    b. Cole Hamels
    c. Yu Darvish
    d. Colby Lewis

15. Which former Rangers manager is quoted as saying, "I've found in life the more you practice, the better you get. If you want something enough and work hard to get it, your chances of success are greater."?

    a. Ted Williams
    b. Don Zimmer
    c. Johnny Oates
    d. Jeff Banister

16. Rangers legend Iván "Pudge" Rodriguez once said, "Never allow the fear of striking out keep you from playing the game."

    a. True
    b. False

17. Sammy Sosa is quoted as saying, "If you have a bad day in baseball and start thinking about it, you will have ____ more."

    a. No
    b. Even

c. 10
d. 100

18. Which former Rangers player once said, "The biggest thing I've learned over the last few years is not looking at the big picture but focusing on that one-day-at-a-time mentality."?

a. Rafael Palmeiro
b. Mark Teixeira
c. Joey Gallo
d. Josh Hamilton

19. Which former Giants manager said, "Be anything you want to be, but don't be dull."?

a. Jim Davenport
b. Alvin Dark
c. John McGraw
d. Frank Robinson

20. Gaylord Perry once said, "The trouble with baseball is that it is not played the year round."

a. True
b. False

QUIZ ANSWERS

1. C – *Moneyball*
2. B – Vladimir Guerrero
3. D – Buck Showalter
4. B – Jim Sundberg
5. D – Iván Rodriguez
6. C – Nolan Ryan
7. B – Adrián Beltré
8. B – False, Jackie Robinson said this.
9. C – Alex Rodriguez
10. A – Nolan Ryan
11. B – Michael Young
12. A – Mark Teixeira
13. C – Rougned Odor
14. B – Cole Hamels
15. A – Ted Williams
16. B – False, Babe Ruth said this.
17. C – 10
18. D – Josh Hamilton
19. D – Frank Robinson
20. A – True

DID YOU KNOW?

1. "Every hitter likes fastballs, just like everybody likes ice cream. But you don't like it when someone's stuffing it into you by the gallon. That's what it feels like when Nolan Ryan's throwin' balls by you." – Reggie Jackson

2. "Through everything, you were there. Through the losing when I first got here, you were there. From me growing up in this park, you were there. Through the best of times, when we were making October noise, you were there. Tonight, here you are again. There is no way I can repay your support and friendship throughout the years. My only hope is that you knew that when I played, I did the best for my teammates, for this uniform, and for all of you. Thank you for everything you have given me over the years. I will always be grateful, and I will always be a Ranger." – Michael Young at his number 10 Retirement Ceremony in 2019

3. "When I first came here, I didn't know what to expect. The first guy I talked to was Michael Young. I'm so grateful for tonight. Last but not least, I want to thank you, the fans, for supporting me and supporting our organization." – Adrián Beltré at his number 29 Retirement Ceremony in 2019

4. "Respect the game, love this game. Sometimes dreams come true. Look at me. I am here on this stage, this special

place, and my dream has become a reality. God bless baseball." – Iván "Pudge" Rodriguez in his National Baseball Hall of Fame induction speech in 2017

5. "When I went to the Texas Rangers as a free agent, I went with the intent to stay one year and finish my career there. And I stayed five. The reason I stayed five is because of the Texas Rangers. I've never enjoyed an organization more than the staff and the ownership there. I appreciate all that they have done for me." – Nolan Ryan in his National Baseball Hall of Fame induction speech in 1999.

6. "From baseball, I developed a thick skin against criticism. I learned to overlook minor setbacks and focus on the long haul."

7. "I don't know how I fell in love with baseball, I just loved to play it. Everyone who loves baseball can remember the first time he saw the inside of a real major league park with real big-league players. It stays with you forever—the greenness of the grass, the sight of major-leaguers in uniform, the sound of a big-league swing meeting a big-league pitch."

8. "I never dreamed about being President, I wanted to be Willie Mays."

9. "It's such a wonderful sport. There aren't any time limits, which means you can go and enjoy yourself. It's a great place to go and relax. It's a wonderful place to visit with somebody you love. It's an important part of our history."

10. "One of the great things about living here (in the White

House) is that you don't have to sign up for a baseball fantasy camp to meet your heroes. It turns out, they come here."

11. Former United States President and former Texas Rangers owner, George W. Bush
12. "You don't have to look like an Under Armour mannequin to be an athlete. A lot of people probably think I'm not athletic or don't even try to work out or whatever, but I do. Just because you're big doesn't mean you can't be an athlete. And just because you work out doesn't mean you're going to have a 12-pack." – Prince Fielder
13. "I'm not perfect. Nobody's perfect. But I love baseball and I love to play hard." – Adrián Beltré
14. "He's (Rafael Palmeiro) always the left-handed swing you want to copy. He's got a real smooth swing and he's never off balance. He's always on top of the ball. I just like watching him hit." – Former Yankees catcher, Jorge Posada
15. "It helps if the hitter thinks you're a little crazy." – Nolan Ryan

CHAPTER 4:

CATCHY NICKNAMES

QUIZ TIME!

1. What nickname did Joey Gallo have on the back of his jersey for Players' Weekend?
    a. Rooster
    b. Pico de Gallo
    c. Joey G
    d. J Money
2. Iván Rodriguez did not go by the nickname "Pudge" until he became a Ranger.
    a. True
    b. False
3. What nickname has former Ranger Juan Gonzalez been going by since he was nine years old?
    a. Juany G
    b. Juan Gone
    c. Igor
    d. Gone Juan

4. What is the nickname of former Rangers pitcher Nolan Ryan?

    a. The Ryan Express
    b. The Life of Ryan
    c. Rollin' Nolan
    d. Flyin' Ryan

5. Which is NOT a nickname the Rangers as a team have been referred to as?

    a. The Power Rangers
    b. The Rags
    c. The Lone Stars
    d. The Blue and Red

6. What nickname did Adrián Beltré's uncle give him as a kid?

    a. Belty
    b. Estrella
    c. Kojak
    d. Gran Chico

7. Kenny Rogers's nickname was "The Gambler," after a song by the singer who shares his name.

    a. True
    b. False

8. Which nickname does former Ranger Nelson Cruz go by?

    a. Aplastar
    b. Fuerte
    c. Dominican Dandy
    d. Boomstick

9. During 2017's MLB Players' Weekend, what nickname did former Rangers pitcher Jason Grilli have on the back of his jersey?
   a. Put It on the Grill
   b. Grill Cheese
   c. All up in my Grill
   d. Grill Chicken
10. Which nickname did MLB Hall-of-Famer and former Ranger Vladimir Guerrero NOT go by in his career?
    a. Vlad the Impaler
    b. Big Daddy Vladdy
    c. Make 'Em Sad Vlad
    d. Big Bad Vlad
11. "Goose" is his nickname. What is the real name of former Rangers pitcher Goose Gossage?
    a. Maxwell William
    b. Richard Michael
    c. Kevin Arthur
    d. Bartholomew Robert
12. Former Rangers pitcher Cliff Lee's real first name is Clifton.
    a. True
    b. False
13. Jarrod Saltalamacchia's last name, at 14 letters, is the longest last name in MLB history. It means "jump over" in Italian. What was Saltalamacchia's nickname?

a. Salt
b. Mach
c. J Salt
d. Salty

14. What is the nickname of former Rangers pitcher Derek Holland?

    a. Holly
    b. Dutch Oven
    c. Dutch Derek
    d. Daunting Derek

15. Former Ranger Will Clark went by the nickname "Will the Thrill."

    a. True
    b. False

16. What is former Rangers pitcher C.J. Wilson's full name?

    a. Cody James Wilson
    b. Christopher James Wilson
    c. Christopher John Wilson
    d. Cody John Wilson

17. Former Rangers infielder Michael Young went by the nickname "Young Blood."

    a. True
    b. False

18. Former Rangers manager Showalter goes by the nickname "Buck." What is his real name?

a. Bruce Nathaniel Showalter III
b. Bruce William Showalter III
c. William Edward Showalter III
d. William Nathaniel Showalter III

19. During 2017's MLB Players' Weekend, what nickname did former Rangers pitcher A.J. Griffin have on the back of his jersey?

a. Arthur Joseph
b. Griff
c. Sweet Lettuce
d. HAIR

20. What is the nickname of former Rangers first baseman Mark Teixeira?

a. Tex
b. Marky T
c. Tex Mex
d. M.T.

QUIZ ANSWERS

1. B – Pico de Gallo
2. A – True
3. C – Igor (He was obsessed with a wrestler, Igor the Magnificent, when he was a kid.)
4. A – The Ryan Express
5. D – The Blue and Red
6. C – Kojak (That was the name of a bald-headed detective on TV at the time, and even as a kid, Adrián didn't have much hair.)
7. A – True
8. D – Boomstick
9. B – Grill Cheese
10. C – Make 'Em Sad Vlad
11. B – Richard Michael
12. A – True
13. D – Salty
14. B – Dutch Oven
15. A – True
16. C – Christopher John Wilson
17. B – False

18. D – William Nathaniel Showalter III

19. C – Sweet Lettuce

20. A – Tex

DID YOU KNOW?

1. Former Rangers second baseman Ian Kinsler was given the nickname "Bootsie" by Ron Washington in 2007. Kinsler missed a month of the season due to a stress fracture and when Wash saw him in a walking boot, the nickname was born. Kinsler even used the nickname "Bootsie" on the back of his Players' Weekend jersey when he was a member of the Detroit Tigers.
2. Both C.J. Wilson and C.J. Nitkowski pitched for the Rangers. Their initials stand for "Christopher John" in both cases.
3. "R.A." is R.A. Dickey's nickname. His full name is Robert Allen Dickey.
4. Rusty Greer pitched his entire nine-year career with the Rangers. His real name is Thurman Clyde Greer III.
5. Former Rangers outfielder Ruben Sierra went by the nickname "El Caballo," which means "the Horse" in Spanish.
6. Former Rangers pitcher Bartolo Colón goes by the nickname "The Big Sexy." It is even the title of his upcoming book.
7. Delino DeShields nicknamed Prince Fielder "Uncle Phil."
8. Catcher A.J. Pierzynski played one season for the Rangers. His full name is Anthony John Pierzynski.

9. During Players' Weekend in 2018 and 2019, Delino DeShields put the nickname "Lil Bop" on the back of his jersey. His dad's nickname was "Bop" when he played in the major leagues.
10. During Players' Weekend in 2019, former Ranger Hunter Pence put the "¯_(ツ)_/¯" emoji on the back of his jersey. He claimed he has no nickname and simply likes this emoji.

CHAPTER 5:

THE RYAN EXPRESS

QUIZ TIME!

1. What is Nolan Ryan's full name?
   a. Nolan Lyle Ryan Jr.
   b. Lyle Nolan Ryan Jr.
   c. Lynn Nolan Ryan Jr.
   d. Nolan Lynn Ryan Jr.
2. During his MLB career, Nolan Ryan played for the Texas Rangers, Houston Astros, New York Mets, and the California Angels.
   a. True
   b. False
3. Where was Nolan Ryan born?
   a. Houston, Texas
   b. Refugio, Texas
   c. Frisco, Texas
   d. Dallas, Texas

4. When was Nolan Ryan born?

    a. January 13, 1947
    b. January 13, 1950
    c. January 31, 1950
    d. January 31, 1947

5. Nolan Ryan threw seven no-hitters in his MLB career.

    a. True
    b. False

6. How many MLB records does Nolan Ryan currently hold?

    a. 61
    b. 51
    c. 41
    d. 31

7. Where did Nolan Ryan go to high school?

    a. Alvin High School
    b. Clear Creek High School
    c. Westwood High School
    d. Carroll High School

8. When Nolan Ryan was called up to the New York Mets in 1966, he was the second-youngest player in the MLB.

    a. True
    b. False

9. Nolan Ryan was previously _______ of the Texas Rangers organization.

    a. General manager
    b. CEO

c. Executive advisor
d. Head scout

10. What is the name of Nolan Ryan's 1992 autobiography?

 a. *Nolan Ryan's Pitcher's Bible*
 b. *Throwing Heat*
 c. *Miracle Man*
 d. *The Road to Cooperstown*

11. Nolan Ryan played in the MLB for how many presidential administrations?

 a. 3
 b. 5
 c. 7
 d. 9

12. Nolan Ryan is one of only three players in MLB history to have his uniform number retired by at least three teams.

 a. True
 b. False

13. What year was Nolan Ryan inducted into the National Baseball Hall of Fame?

 a. 1995
 b. 1989
 c. 1990
 d. 1999

14. Nolan Ryan NEVER threw a Perfect Game and NEVER won a Cy Young Award.

a. True
b. False

15. Nolan Ryan is one of only 29 players in MLB history to pitch in ____ different decades.

a. 3
b. 4
c. 5
d. 6

16. Nolan Ryan was drafted by the ____________________.

a. Texas Rangers
b. Houston Astros
c. California Angels
d. New York Mets

17. There is a Nolan Ryan statue in front of Globe Life Park.

a. True
b. False

18. How many All-Star Games was Nolan Ryan named to during his career?

a. 7
b. 8
c. 9
d. 10

19. Nolan Ryan has a charity whose mission is "to provide resources for youth, education and community development." What is the name of Ryan's charity?

a. The Ryan Express Foundation
b. The Ryan Foundation
c. The Nolan Ryan Foundation
d. The Nolan Foundation

20. Nolan Ryan used to soak his fingers in pickle juice to avoid and treat blisters.

    a. True
    b. False

QUIZ ANSWERS

1. C – Lynn Nolan Ryan Jr.
2. A – True
3. B – Refugio, Texas
4. D – January 31, 1947
5. A – True
6. B – 51
7. A – Alvin High School
8. A – True
9. B – CEO
10. C – *Miracle Man*
11. C – 7: Lyndon B. Johnson, Richard Nixon, Gerald Ford, Jimmy Carter, Ronald Reagan, George H.W. Bush, and Bill Clinton
12. A – True
13. D – 1999
14. A – True
15. B – 4
16. D – New York Mets
17. A – True
18. B – 8
19. C – The Nolan Ryan Foundation
20. A – True

DID YOU KNOW?

1. Nolan Ryan married his high school sweetheart, Ruth.
2. In May 2000, Nolan Ryan introduced Nolan Ryan Tender Age Beef to Texas markets. The beef was raised and sold on Ryan's personal ranch.
3. From August 2010 to October 2013, Nolan Ryan was a part-owner of the Texas Rangers.
4. In May 2014, Nolan Ryan published a cookbook called *The Nolan Ryan Beef and Barbecue Cookbook: Recipes from a Texas Kitchen*, which included more than 75 recipes.
5. In November 2016, Nolan Ryan, along with David Ortiz and Barry Larkin, created Dugout Ventures, an equity group that focuses on baseball products and companies.
6. Nolan Ryan suffered a heart attack in April 2000 and underwent emergency double bypass surgery.
7. Nolan Ryan had an infamous fight/brawl with Robin Ventura in 1993 at Arlington Stadium.
8. Nolan Ryan used to be a newspaper boy. He delivered copies of the *Houston Post* every morning for several years.
9. Nolan Ryan played in the MLB for 27 years.
10. The New York Mets are the only team Ryan played for that has not retired his number. The Rangers, Astros, and Angels have.

CHAPTER 6:

STATISTICALLY SPEAKING

QUIZ TIME!

1. Juan Gonzalez holds the Texas Rangers franchise record for the most home runs. How many did he hit?
   a. 321
   b. 372
   c. 246
   d. 217
2. Pitcher Charlie Hough has the most wins in Texas Rangers franchise history, with 139.
   a. True
   b. False
3. How many times have the Rangers made the playoffs?
   a. 8 times
   b. 10 times
   c. 12 times
   d. 7 times

4. Who holds the Rangers' single-season record for doubles with 52 in 2006?

    a. Elvis Andrus
    b. Michael Young
    c. Mark Teixeira
    d. Nelson Cruz

5. Which pitcher has the most strikeouts in Rangers franchise history, with 1,452?

    a. Kenny Rogers
    b. Yu Darvish
    c. Nolan Ryan
    d. Charlie Hough

6. Juan Gonzalez has the most RBI in Rangers franchise history, with ________.

    a. 984
    b. 1,230
    c. 1,180
    d. 842

7. Bobby Valentine is the Rangers' all-time winningest manager.

    a. True
    b. False

8. Which player holds the record for most saves in franchise history, with 150?

    a. Neftalí Feliz
    b. John Wetteland

c. C.J. Wilson
d. Joe Nathan

9. Which player holds the Rangers franchise record for stolen bases, with 302?
   a. Elvis Andrus
   b. Ian Kinsler
   c. Delino DeShields
   d. Bump Wills

10. Who holds the single-season Rangers record for hits, with 221?
    a. Mickey Rivers
    b. Rafael Palmeiro
    c. Alex Rodriguez
    d. Michael Young

11. Who holds the single-season Rangers record for home runs, with 57?
    a. Frank Howard
    b. Juan Gonzalez
    c. Alex Rodriguez
    d. Rafael Palmeiro

12. Adrián Beltré hit the most sacrifice flies in Rangers franchise history.
    a. True
    b. False

13. Who threw the most wild pitches in Rangers franchise history, with 99?

a. Bobby Witt
b. Nolan Ryan
c. Charlie Hough
d. Kevin Brown

14. Who holds the Rangers' single-season record for triples, with 14?

a. Ruben Sierra
b. Marty Keough
c. Chuck Hinton
d. Rougned Odor

15. Which player has the most walks in Rangers franchise history, with 805?

a. Shin-Soo Choo
b. Rusty Greer
c. Mike Hargrove
d. Rafael Palmeiro

16. Which Rangers hitter holds the single-season record for most strikeouts, with 207?

a. Mike Napoli
b. Joey Gallo
c. Josh Hamilton
d. Ian Desmond

17. Michael Young has the most hits, doubles, and triples in Rangers franchise history.

a. True
b. False

18. Which player has the most plate appearances in Rangers franchise history, with 8,047?

    a. Iván Rodriguez
    b. Elvis Andrus
    c. Michael Young
    d. Adrián Beltré

19. Which pitcher holds the Rangers franchise record for most saves in a single season, with 49?

    a. Joe Nathan
    b. Neftalí Feliz
    c. John Wetteland
    d. Francisco Cordero

20. Kenny Rogers allowed the most hits in Rangers franchise history, with 1,997.

    a. True
    b. False

QUIZ ANSWERS

1. B – 372
2. A – True
3. A – 8 times
4. B – Michael Young
5. D – Charlie Hough
6. C – 1,180
7. B – False, Ron Washington holds that record.
8. B – John Wetteland
9. A – Elvis Andrus
10. D – Michael Young
11. C – Alex Rodriguez
12. B – False, Michael Young holds that record.
13. C – Charlie Hough
14. A – Ruben Sierra
15. D – Rafael Palmeiro
16. B – Joey Gallo
17. A – True
18. C – Michael Young
19. D – Francisco Cordero
20. A – True

DID YOU KNOW?

1. Charlie Hough threw the most innings in Rangers franchise history, with 2,308. Coming in second is Kenny Rogers with 1,909 innings.
2. Al Oliver has the best career batting average in Rangers franchise history at .319. Will Clark is second with a career batting average of .308.
3. Ian Kinsler holds the Rangers franchise record for stolen base percentage, with 80.37% success. Elvis Andrus holds the franchise records for career stolen bases, with 302, and for number of times caught stealing, with 104.
4. Juan Gonzalez has the most extra-base hits in Rangers franchise history, with 713. Second on the list is Rafael Palmeiro with 667.
5. Alex Rodriguez holds the Rangers franchise record for at-bats per home run, with 11.9. This means that during his time with Texas, A-Rod hit a home run every 11 to 12 at-bats.
6. Craig Gentry, Jurickson Profar, and Michael Young are all tied for the Rangers' single-season record for stolen base percentage at 100! During the season, they were never thrown out while stealing a base. Incredible!
7. Robinson Chirinos and Carlos Gomez are tied for the Rangers' single-season record for the most times hit by a pitch. Each was hit 19 times.

8. Bert "Campy" Campaneris holds both the first and second spots for most single-season sacrifice hits in Rangers franchise history. He had 40 sacrifice hits in 1977 and 25 sacrifice hits the season after.

9. Fergie Jenkins holds the Rangers' single-season record for wins, with 25 in 1974. Second on the list is Kevin Brown with 21 in 1992.

10. Denny McLain holds the Rangers' single-season record for most losses, with 22 in 1971. Charlie Hough has the most losses in Rangers franchise history, with 123. (He also holds the record for wins.)

CHAPTER 7:

THE TRADE MARKET

QUIZ TIME!

1. At the trade deadline in 2007, the Rangers acquired Jarrod Saltalamacchia, Elvis Andrus, Matt Harrison, Neftalí Feliz, and Beau Jones from the Atlanta Braves in exchange for _______________ and Ron Mahay.
    a. Nelson Cruz
    b. Sammy Sosa
    c. Mark Teixeira
    d. Marlon Byrd
2. On July 19, 2000, the Rangers traded Esteban Loaiza to the Toronto Blue Jays in exchange for __________ and Darwin Cubillán.
    a. Rafael Palmeiro
    b. Kenny Rogers
    c. Iván Rodriguez
    d. Michael Young
3. In December 2007, Josh Hamilton was traded to the Rangers by the Cincinnati Reds.

a. True
b. False

4. On February 16, 2004, the Rangers acquired Alfonso Soriano and Joaquin Arias from the New York Yankees in exchange for ________________.

   a. Juan Gonzalez
   b. Alex Rodriguez
   c. Ryan Christenson
   d. Rafael Palmeiro

5. At the trade deadline in 2015, the Rangers gave up six players in exchange for Cole Hamels and Jake Diekman.

   a. True
   b. False

6. What year did the Rangers trade Juan Gonzalez to the Detroit Tigers?

   a. 1997
   b. 1998
   c. 1999
   d. 2000

7. In 1989, the Rangers traded ________________, Wilson Alvarez, and Scott Fletcher to the Chicago White Sox in exchange for Harold Baines and Fred Manrique.

   a. Cecil Espy
   b. Ruben Sierra
   c. Rick Leach
   d. Sammy Sosa

8. Which team traded Cliff Lee to the Rangers in 2010?

    a. Cleveland Indians
    b. Philadelphia Phillies
    c. Seattle Mariners
    d. Tampa Bay Rays

9. On August 31, 1992, the Rangers traded Ruben Sierra, Bobby Witt, and Jeff Russell to the Oakland A's in exchange for ________________.

    a. Jose Canseco
    b. Rickey Henderson
    c. Mark McGwire
    d. Dave Stewart

10. In order to acquire Jeff Kent in 1996, the Giants sent third baseman Matt Williams to the Cleveland Indians.

    a. True
    b. False

11. On November 20, 2013, the Rangers traded Ian Kinsler to the Detroit Tigers in exchange for ______________.

    a. Miguel Cabrera
    b. Prince Fielder
    c. Austin Jackson
    d. Brandon Inge

12. The Rangers have so far (as of 2019) made only three trades with the Arizona Diamondbacks ever.

    a. True
    b. False

13. How many trades have the Rangers made with the Houston Astros all time (as of the end of the 2019 season)?

    a. 3
    b. 10
    c. 12
    d. 15

14. The Rangers have NEVER made a trade with the Washington Nationals.

    a. True
    b. False

15. After spending five years with the Rangers, Josh Hamilton signed as a free agent with the Los Angeles Angels of Anaheim. In 2015, he was traded back to the Rangers by the Angels.

    a. True
    b. False

16. At the trade deadline in 2017, the Rangers traded __________ to the Los Angeles Dodgers in exchange for A.J. Alexy, Brendon Davis, and Willie Calhoun.

    a. Andrew Cashner
    b. Cole Hamels
    c. A.J. Griffin
    d. Yu Darvish

17. On August 7, 2015, the _______________ sent Mike Napoli and cash to the Rangers for a player to be named later and cash.

a. Boston Red Sox
b. Los Angeles Angels of Anaheim
c. Cleveland Indians
d. New York Yankees

18. On December 15, 2019, the Cleveland Indians traded ____________ and cash to the Rangers for Delino DeShields and Emmanuel Clase.

a. Lance Lynn
b. Mike Minor
c. Corey Kluber
d. Drew Smyly

19. The Rangers have made ___ trades with the Colorado Rockies in franchise history (as of June 2020).

a. 1
b. 5
c. 8
d. 19

20. On June 6, 2003, the Rangers traded Ruben Sierra to the New York Yankees in exchange for Marcus Thames.

a. True
b. False

QUIZ ANSWERS

1. C – Mark Teixeira
2. D – Michael Young
3. A – True
4. B – Alex Rodriguez
5. A – True
6. C – 1999
7. D – Sammy Sosa
8. C – Seattle Mariners
9. A – Jose Canseco
10. A – True
11. B – Prince Fielder
12. A – True
13. B – 10
14. B – False
15. A – True
16. D – Yu Darvish
17. A – Boston Red Sox
18. C – Corey Kluber
19. B – 5
20. A – True

DID YOU KNOW?

1. The Texas Rangers had the 20th largest payroll in Major League Baseball in 2019 at $106.96 million. The Chicago Cubs held the spot for the largest payroll at over $211 million.
2. On December 9, 2012, the Rangers traded Michael Young and cash to the Philadelphia Phillies in exchange for Lisalverto Bonilla and Josh Lindblom.
3. Nolan Ryan signed as a free agent with the Texas Rangers on December 7, 1988. He finished his career with the Rangers in 1993.
4. The Rangers have made 14 trades with the San Francisco Giants all time (as of June 2020).
5. On December 8, 2005, the Texas Rangers traded Alfonso Soriano to the Washington Nationals in exchange for Armando Galarraga, Terrmel Sledge, and Brad Wilkerson. The Rangers originally acquired Soriano from Yankees in the Alex Rodriguez trade.
6. On January 6, 2006, the Rangers traded Adrián Gonzalez, Terrmel Sledge, and Chris Young to the San Diego Padres in exchange for Adam Eaton, Billy Killian, and Akinori Otsuka.
7. On January 5, 2011, Adrián Beltré signed as a free agent with the Texas Rangers. He stayed with the Rangers until he retired in 2018.

8. Kenny Rogers had three stints with the Texas Rangers. He was drafted by them and signed with them as a free agent twice.
9. On July 30, 2011, the Baltimore Orioles traded Koji Uehara to the Texas Rangers in exchange for Chris Martin and Tommy Hunter.
10. At the trade deadline in 2012, the Rangers traded Kyle Hendricks and Christian Villanueva to the Chicago Cubs in exchange for Ryan Dempster.

CHAPTER 8:

DRAFT DAY

QUIZ TIME!

1. With the ___ overall pick in the 1st round of the 2001 MLB Draft, the Texas Rangers selected infielder Mark Teixeira.
   a. 1st
   b. 2nd
   c. 5th
   d. 10th
2. With the 18th overall pick in the 1st round of the 1996 MLB Draft, the Texas Rangers selected __________.
   a. Carlos Peña
   b. R.A. Dickey
   c. Kevin Brown
   d. Bobby Witt
3. With the 11th overall pick in the 1st round of the 2008 MLB Draft, the Texas Rangers selected first baseman Justin Smoak from ________________.
   a. Clemson University
   b. University of South Carolina

c. College of Charleston
d. University of North Carolina at Chapel Hill

4. With the ___ overall pick in the 1st round of the 1969 MLB Draft, the Texas Rangers selected outfielder Jeff Burroughs.

a. 1st
b. 3rd
c. 4th
d. 9th

5. With the 4th overall pick in the 1st round of the 2015 MLB Draft, the Texas Rangers selected pitcher Dillon Tate from ____________________.

a. UC Davis
b. UCLA
c. UC San Diego
d. UC Santa Barbara

6. Pitcher Ron Darling was drafted by the Texas Rangers in the _____ round of the 1981 MLB Draft out of Yale University.

a. 3rd
b. 6th
c. 9th
d. 11th

7. The Texas Rangers drafted Joey Gallo in the 1st round of the 2012 MLB Draft, 39th overall. Instead of enrolling at LSU, he signed with the Rangers for a $2.25 million signing bonus.

a. True
b. False

8. Pitcher Kenny Rogers was drafted in the 39th round of the _____ MLB Draft by the Texas Rangers.

    a. 1980
    b. 1981
    c. 1982
    d. 1983

9. With the 1st overall pick in the 1st round of the 1999 MLB draft, the ___________ selected outfielder Josh Hamilton.

    a. Texas Rangers
    b. Los Angeles Angels of Anaheim
    c. Tampa Bay Devil Rays
    d. Cincinnati Reds

10. Harold Baines was drafted 1st overall in the 1st round of the 1977 MLB Draft by the Chicago White Sox.

    a. True
    b. False

11. In the 8th round of the 1966 MLB Draft, the _________ selected pitcher Charlie Hough.

    a. Florida Marlins
    b. Los Angeles Dodgers
    c. Chicago White Sox
    d. Texas Rangers

12. Alex Rodriguez was drafted 1st overall in the 1st round of the 1993 MLB Draft by the Seattle Mariners.

a. True
b. False

13. The Texas Rangers selected pitcher ____________ in the 25th round of the 2006 MLB Draft.

    a. Jason Grilli
    b. C.J. Wilson
    c. Brandon McCarthy
    d. Derek Holland

14. The Texas Rangers selected pitcher ____________ in the 5th round of the 2001 MLB Draft.

    a. R.A. Dickey
    b. C.J. Wilson
    c. Kenny Rogers
    d. Scott Feldman

15. Current Texas Rangers manager Chris Woodward was drafted in the 54th round of the 1994 MLB Draft by the _______________.

    a. New York Mets
    b. Boston Red Sox
    c. Toronto Blue Jays
    d. Atlanta Braves

16. Former Texas Rangers pitcher Cole Hamels was drafted in the 1st round of the 2002 MLB Draft by the _____________.

    a. Chicago Cubs
    b. Philadelphia Phillies
    c. Los Angeles Dodgers
    d. New York Yankees

17. In the 17th round of the 2007 MLB Draft, the Texas Rangers selected ________________.

    a. Geovany Soto
    b. Ian Kinsler
    c. Craig Gentry
    d. Mitch Moreland

18. What college was first baseman Carlos Peña drafted out of?

    a. Boston College
    b. Harvard University
    c. Northeastern University
    d. University of Massachusetts Boston

19. In the 1st round of the 2020 MLB Draft, the Texas Rangers selected second baseman ______________ 14th overall out of Mississippi State.

    a. Justin Foscue
    b. Evan Carter
    c. Tekoah Roby
    d. Dylan MacLean

20. Rafael Palmeiro was drafted by the New York Mets in the 8th round of the 1982 MLB Draft and then again in the 22nd round of the 1985 MLB Draft by the Chicago Cubs.

    a. True
    b. False

QUIZ ANSWERS

1. C – 5th
2. B – R.A. Dickey
3. B – University of South Carolina
4. A – 1st
5. D – UC Santa Barbara
6. C – 9th
7. A – True
8. C – 1982
9. C – Tampa Bay Devil Rays
10. A – True
11. B – Los Angeles Dodgers
12. A – True
13. D – Derek Holland
14. B – C.J. Wilson
15. C – Toronto Blue Jays
16. B – Philadelphia Phillies
17. D – Mitch Moreland
18. C – Northeastern University
19. A – Justin Foscue
20. A – True

DID YOU KNOW?

1. In the 1st round of the 1999 MLB Draft, the Texas Rangers selected pitcher Colby Lewis.
2. Ian Kinsler was drafted three different times. By the Arizona Diamondbacks in 2000 and 2001 and finally by the Rangers in 2003, where he ultimately signed.
3. Scott Feldman was drafted by the Houston Astros in 2002 and again by the Texas Rangers in 2003.
4. Former Rangers pitcher Brandon McCarthy was drafted by the Chicago White Sox in the 17th round of the 2002 MLB Draft.
5. Former Rangers outfielder Marlon Byrd was drafted by the Philadelphia Phillies in the 10th round of the 1999 MLB Draft.
6. Jarrod Saltalamacchia was drafted by the Atlanta Braves in the 1st round of the 2003 MLB Draft.
7. Adrián Gonzalez was drafted by the Florida Marlins 1st overall in the 1st round of the 2000 MLB Draft out of high school.
8. Delino DeShields was drafted in the 1st round of the 2010 MLB Draft by the Houston Astros.
9. Mike Napoli was drafted in the 17th round of the 2000 MLB Draft by the Anaheim Angels.

10. Ryan Dempster was drafted in the 3rd round of the 1995 MLB Draft by the Texas Rangers, but he did not play for the Rangers until 2012.

CHAPTER 9:

ODDS & ENDS

QUIZ TIME!

1. Adrián Beltré hates when people touch his __________.

   a. Feet
   b. Shoulder
   c. Ear
   d. Head

2. Prince Fielder was named after the musician Prince because his mother was a huge fan of the singer.

   a. True
   b. False

3. On May 26, 1993, Jose Canseco let a fly ball bounce off his _______ and over the outfield wall, resulting in a home run for Cleveland Indians infielder Carlos Martinez.

   a. Arm
   b. Leg
   c. Head
   d. Foot

4. Which former Ranger takes a nap before almost every game he plays in as a pregame ritual?

    a. Yu Darvish
    b. Mitch Moreland
    c. Ian Kinsler
    d. Nelson Cruz

5. When he was 8 years old, former Ranger Prince Fielder starred in a __________ commercial. He struck out his father, Cecil, a former MLB player himself.

    a. Chevrolet
    b. McDonald's
    c. Coca-Cola
    d. Disneyland

6. Which former Ranger coached the American League in the 2010 Taco Bell All-Star Legends & Celebrity Softball Game?

    a. Goose Gossage
    b. Nolan Ryan
    c. Iván Rodriguez
    d. Kenny Rogers

7. Former Ranger Jose Canseco has a twin brother who also played in the MLB.

    a. True
    b. False

8. Former Ranger Adrián Gonzalez's brother-in-law (his wife's brother) also plays in the MLB. Who is his brother-in-law?

a. Bryce Harper
b. Kris Bryant
c. Manny Machado
d. Clayton Kershaw

9. Which former Ranger appeared in a Guitar Hero World Tour commercial playing guitar alongside Kobe Bryant on vocals, Michael Phelps on bass, and Tony Hawk on drums?

   a. Nolan Ryan
   b. Alex Rodriguez
   c. Adrián Beltré
   d. Iván Rodriguez

10. Former Rangers pitcher Yu Darvish can guess someone's ________________ by simply engaging in a conversation with them and getting to know their personality.

    a. Favorite color
    b. Astrological sign
    c. Age
    d. Blood type

11. Former Rangers pitcher Derek Holland was once kicked out of a ________________ concert in New Jersey.

    a. One Direction
    b. Bruce Springsteen
    c. Counting Crows
    d. Ariana Grande

12. Former Ranger Fergie Jenkins also played basketball for the Harlem Globetrotters.

a. True
b. False

13. What does Josh Hamilton have tattooed on his left arm?

    a. A portrait of Alexander Hamilton
    b. "Hambone"
    c. A pig
    d. "Hammy"

14. Which former Ranger is now an analyst for MLB Network?

    a. Mark DeRosa
    b. Tim Lincecum
    c. Aubrey Huff
    d. Cody Ross

15. Which country music artist did Rangers infielder Elvis Andrus listen to when he was a teenager to help him learn English?

    a. Carrie Underwood
    b. Shania Twain
    c. Rascal Flatts
    d. Tim McGraw

16. The same owner who moved the NBA's Lakers from Minneapolis to Los Angeles was the owner who moved the Rangers from Washington to Arlington.

    a. True
    b. False

17. Former Rangers pitcher C.J. Wilson holds a charitable event each year featuring which popular video game?

a. *Mario Party*
b. *Fortnite*
c. *Call of Duty*
d. *Guitar Hero*

18. In which city does the Rangers' Double-A team play?

a. Sacramento, California
b. Indianapolis, Indiana
c. Sioux Falls, South Dakota
d. Frisco, Texas

19. Who is the first and only Rangers pitcher to throw a perfect game?

a. Kenny Rogers
b. Nolan Ryan
c. Cole Hamels
d. Yu Darvish

20. Former Rangers catcher Taylor Teagarden won a bronze medal at the 2008 Summer Olympics in Beijing as a member of the USA baseball team.

a. True
b. False

QUIZ ANSWERS

1. D – Head
2. A – True
3. C – Head
4. D – Nelson Cruz
5. B – McDonald's
6. A – Goose Gossage
7. A – True, His name is Ozzie Canseco.
8. C – Manny Machado
9. B – Alex Rodriguez
10. D – Blood type
11. C – Counting Crows
12. A – True
13. B – "Hambone"
14. A – Mark DeRosa
15. C – Rascal Flatts
16. A – True
17. D – *Guitar Hero*
18. D – Frisco, Texas (the Frisco Roughriders at Dr. Pepper Ballpark)
19. A – Kenny Rogers
20. A – True

DID YOU KNOW?

1. Back in 1998, former Ranger Alex Rodriguez was asked by a reporter who his dream date would be with. His answer? Jennifer Lopez. And 22 years later, J-Lo and A-Rod are engaged to be married.
2. Charlie Hough is the uncle of Julianne and Derek Hough, both professional dancers on ABC's *Dancing with the Stars.*
3. Former Rangers pitcher Colby Lewis was the first MLB player to ever take paternity leave.
4. According to *Ballpark Digest,* the dimensions of Globe Life Field were chosen to honor key moments and people in Texas Rangers history: "Left Field Line: 329 feet (Adrián Beltré's #29); Left Field Power Alley: 372 feet (Rangers' first year in Arlington–1972); Center Field (straightaway): 407 feet (Iván Rodriguez's #7); Deepest Distance of Park (both left and right of straightaway CF): 410 feet (Michael Young's #10); Right Field Power Alley: 374 (The Turnaround Gang, 57 to 84 wins–1974); Right Field Line: 326 feet (Johnny Oates's #26)."
5. Derek Holland's nickname is "Dutch Oven" because of his last name. It is even his handle on Twitter (@Dutch_Oven45).
6. Former Rangers and current San Francisco Giants manager Gabe Kapler is only the 7th Jewish manager in MLB history. He also went to the same high school as Ice

Cube. Those facts don't really mesh together well, but whatever.

7. During the 1990s and early 2000s, Nolan Ryan was a spokesman for the popular pain reliever Advil.
8. Iván "Pudge" Rodriguez opened Pudge's Pizza at Texas Live!, which is where the Rangers' new ballpark, Globe Life Field, is located.
9. Former Ranger Hunter Pence's wife Lexi has a YouTube channel that often features content with her and Hunter. The channel is called "Let's Get Lexi."
10. Adrián Beltré was once in a J.C. Penney Christmas commercial, but it was not planned. In fact, the people from J.C. Penney didn't recognize or even realize it was him until the ad was released.

CHAPTER 10:
OUTFIELDERS

QUIZ TIME!

1. Which team has former Rangers outfielder Nelson Cruz NOT played for during his career so far (as of the end of the 2019 season)?
    a. Milwaukee Brewers
    b. Detroit Tigers
    c. Seattle Mariners
    d. Baltimore Orioles
2. In 1974, former Rangers outfielder Jeff Burroughs led the American League in RBI and won the American League MVP Award.
    a. True
    b. False
3. Which team did former Rangers outfielder Juan Gonzalez NOT play for during his playing career?
    a. Cleveland Indians
    b. Kansas City Royals

c. Detroit Tigers
d. Florida Marlins

4. Current Ranger Joey Gallo became the fastest player in American League history to hit 100 home runs.

   a. True
   b. False

5. Former Rangers outfielder Gabe Kapler is now manager of which MLB team?

   a. New York Mets
   b. Washington Nationals
   c. San Francisco Giants
   d. Houston Astros

6. How many games did outfielder Delino DeShields play in his 2015 (first) season with the Rangers?

   a. 80
   b. 121
   c. 162
   d. 137

7. Shin-Soo Choo has played his entire career (as of the end of the 2019 season) with the Texas Rangers.

   a. True
   b. False

8. How many seasons did Jose Canseco play for the Rangers?

   a. 1
   b. 2

c. 3
d. 4

9. How many home runs did Hunter Pence hit during his 84 games with the Texas Rangers during the 2019 season?

    a. 8
    b. 18
    c. 28
    d. 1

10. How many seasons did outfielder Josh Hamilton play for the Texas Rangers?

    a. 6
    b. 7
    c. 8
    d. 9

11. Which team did former Rangers outfielder Craig Gentry NOT play for during his 10-year MLB career?

    a. Oakland A's
    b. Los Angeles Angels of Anaheim
    c. Baltimore Orioles
    d. San Diego Padres

12. David Murphy NEVER hit more than 10 home runs during his time with the Texas Rangers.

    a. True
    b. False

13. Mitch Moreland has so far (as of 2019) played for one other MLB team besides the Rangers. Which team is it?

a. Los Angeles Dodgers
b. Minnesota Twins
c. Boston Red Sox
d. Atlanta Braves

14. Former Ranger Vladimir Guerrero's son, Vladimir Guerrero Jr., currently (as of the end of the 2019 season) plays third base for which MLB team?

a. Los Angeles Angels of Anaheim
b. Toronto Blue Jays
c. Baltimore Orioles
d. Texas Rangers

15. What was former Rangers outfielder Alfonso Soriano's season batting average in 2004?

a. .277
b. .260
c. .280
d. .236

16. Sammy Sosa hit only one home run during his 1989 stint with the Rangers and 21 home runs during his 2007 stint with the Rangers.

a. True
b. False

17. How many hits did outfielder Marlon Byrd accumulate for the Rangers during the 2009 season?

a. 135
b. 145

c. 155
d. 165

18. Which team did former Rangers outfielder Jeff Burroughs NOT play for during his 16-year MLB playing career?

    a. Oakland A's
    b. Atlanta Braves
    c. Seattle Mariners
    d. Chicago Cubs

19. How many MLB All-Star Games did former Rangers outfielder Alex Rios play in during his career?

    a. 0
    b. 2
    c. 3
    d. 4

20. Former Rangers outfielder Marlon Byrd played for 10 different MLB teams during his 15-season career.

    a. True
    b. False

QUIZ ANSWERS

1. B – Detroit Tigers
2. A – True
3. D – Florida Marlins
4. A – True
5. C – San Francisco Giants
6. B – 121
7. B – False, He also played with the Seattle Mariners, Cleveland Indians, and Cincinnati Reds.
8. C – 3
9. B – 18
10. A – 6
11. D – San Diego Padres
12. B – False
13. C – Boston Red Sox
14. B – Toronto Blue Jays
15. C – .280
16. A – True
17. C – 155
18. D – Chicago Cubs

19. B – 2

20. A – True, He played for the Philadelphia Phillies, Texas Rangers, Chicago Cubs, Washington Nationals, New York Mets, San Francisco Giants, Pittsburgh Pirates, Boston Red Sox, Cleveland Indians, and Cincinnati Reds.

DID YOU KNOW?

1. Juan Gonzalez played in 1,400 games in his 13 seasons with the Texas Rangers.
2. Jeff Burroughs played 700 games in his seven seasons with the Texas Rangers.
3. Former Rangers outfielder Josh Hamilton had the best batting average in the American League in 2010 at .359.
4. Former Rangers outfielder Nelson Cruz has appeared in six MLB All-Star Games so far in his career (as of the 2019 season). He also has three Silver Slugger Awards, and he won the 2011 AL ALCS MVP Award when he was with the Rangers.
5. Vladimir Guerrero only played one season with the Texas Rangers. During that 2010 season, he hit 29 home runs, played in 152 games, and had 178 hits.
6. Leonys Martín hit only 20 home runs in his five seasons with the Texas Rangers.
7. Jeff Burroughs hit 108 home runs in his seven seasons with the Texas Rangers.
8. Juan Gonzalez hit 372 home runs in his 13 seasons with the Texas Rangers.
9. Josh Hamilton hit 150 home runs in his six seasons with the Texas Rangers.

10. David Murphy hit 85 home runs in his seven seasons with the Texas Rangers. In 826 games, he accumulated 733 hits and 2,666 at-bats.

CHAPTER 11:

INFIELDERS

QUIZ TIME!

1. How many games did former Rangers third baseman Adrián Beltré play in during his eight seasons with the team?

    a. 999
    b. 1,001
    c. 1,232
    d. 1,098

2. As of the end of the 2019 season, former Rangers second baseman Ian Kinsler has appeared in four All-Star Games. All but one of those was as a member of the Rangers.

    a. True
    b. False

3. How many games did former Rangers infielder Michael Young play in during his 13 seasons with the team?

    a. 1,101
    b. 1,823

c. 2,098
d. 1,458

4. Alex Rodriguez played for the Texas Rangers for three seasons and, of course, was with the New York Yankees for 12 seasons. He played for a total of three teams during his 22-season career. Which other MLB team did he play for?

   a. Florida Marlins
   b. San Diego Padres
   c. Seattle Mariners
   d. Los Angeles Dodgers

5. Which MLB team did former Rangers first baseman Mark Teixeira NOT play for during his 14-season career?

   a. New York Yankees
   b. Atlanta Braves
   c. Toronto Blue Jays
   d. Los Angeles Angels of Anaheim

6. How many seasons did Prince Fielder play in the MLB?

   a. 10
   b. 12
   c. 14
   d. 18

7. Michael Young played his entire MLB career with the Texas Rangers.

   a. True
   b. False

8. How many home runs did former Ranger Lance Berkman hit during his one season (73 games played) with the team?
    a. 6
    b. 12
    c. 20
    d. 24
9. How many home runs did Rangers shortstop Elvis Andrus hit during the 2017 season?
    a. 22
    b. 25
    c. 20
    d. 29
10. During his 21-season career, former Rangers third baseman Adrián Beltré appeared in ___ MLB All-Star Games, and he won four Silver Slugger Awards and five Gold Glove Awards.
    a. 2
    b. 3
    c. 4
    d. 7
11. How many hits did former Rangers first baseman Mitch Moreland accumulate during his seven seasons in Texas?
    a. 633
    b. 643
    c. 653

d. 663

12. Rougned Odor played in all 162 games for the Rangers in 2017.

 a. True
 b. False

13. Where was former Rangers first baseman Rafael Palmeiro born?

 a. Puerto Rico
 b. Cuba
 c. Spain
 d. Dominican Republic

14. How many games did first baseman Will Clark play for the Rangers during the 1995 season?

 a. 101
 b. 112
 c. 132
 d. 123

15. How many seasons did Rafael Palmeiro play for the Texas Rangers?

 a. 8
 b. 10
 c. 12
 d. 13

16. Former Rangers third baseman Buddy Bell was NEVER named to an MLB All-Star Game during his career.

a. True
b. False

17. Which infielder did NOT play for BOTH the Rangers AND the Houston Astros during his MLB career?

a. Lance Berkman
b. Ryan Theriot
c. Mark Teixeira
d. Buddy Bell

18. Which infielder did NOT play for BOTH the Rangers AND the Oakland A's during his MLB career?

a. Mike Hargrove
b. Bert Campaneris
c. Kevin Kouzmanoff
d. Jurickson Profar

19. Shortstop Elvis Andrus was named to the MLB All-Star Game in 2010 and _______.

a. 2011
b. 2012
c. 2014
d. 2018

20. Former Rangers first baseman Mike Hargrove was named the American League Rookie of the Year in 1974.

a. True
b. False

QUIZ ANSWERS

1. D – 1,098
2. A – True
3. B – 1,823
4. C – Seattle Mariners
5. C – Toronto Blue Jays
6. B – 12
7. B – False, He also played for the Philadelphia Phillies and Los Angeles Dodgers.
8. A – 6
9. C – 20 (His career-best in a single season as of the 2019 season.)
10. C – 4
11. A – 633
12. A – True
13. B – Cuba
14. D – 123
15. B – 10
16. B – False, He was named to five All-Star Games (1973, 1980, 1981, 1982, 1984).
17. C – Mark Teixeira

18. A – Mike Hargrove

19. B – 2012

20. A – True

DID YOU KNOW?

1. Rangers second baseman Rougned Odor was named the American League Player of the Week on July 26, 2015; September 4, 2016; July 22, 2018; and August 5, 2018.
2. Former Rangers first baseman Rafael Palmeiro was named the American League Player of the Week on May 28, 1989; July 12, 1992; July 4, 1993; August 1, 1993; and August 22, 1999.
3. As of the end of the 2019 season, shortstop Elvis Andrus has appeared in two MLB All-Star Games.
4. Former Rangers infielder Michael Young only won one Gold Glove Award in his career.
5. Former Rangers first baseman Will Clark also played for the San Francisco Giants, Baltimore Orioles, and St. Louis Cardinals during his 15-season MLB career.
6. Both Elvis Andrus and Rougned Odor were born in Venezuela.
7. Infielder Joaquin Arias played for the San Francisco Giants, New York Mets, and Texas Rangers during his career. Before retirement, he was signed by the New York Yankees as a free agent, but he never played for them.
8. Joey Gallo currently (as of 2019) plays in the outfield for the Rangers but used to play third base for the Rangers in previous seasons.

9. Adrián Beltré's personal best for hits in a single season was in 2013 with the Rangers when he accumulated 199 hits in 161 games played.
10. Adrián Beltré won two American League Platinum Gloves during his career in 2011 and 2012.

CHAPTER 12:

PITCHERS & CATCHERS

QUIZ TIME!

1. How many strikeouts did Nolan Ryan record during his 1989 season with the Rangers?

    a. 341
    b. 223
    c. 301
    d. 327

2. Iván "Pudge" Rodriguez hit 217 home runs over the course of his 13 seasons with the Rangers.

    a. True
    b. False

3. Which pitcher has NOT pitched for BOTH the Rangers AND Houston Astros in his MLB career?

    a. Armando Galarraga
    b. Travis Blackley
    c. Cole Hamels
    d. Nolan Ryan

4. Which former Rangers manager was a catcher in his playing career?
    a. Ron Washington
    b. Don Zimmer
    c. Bobby Valentine
    d. Jeff Banister
5. Which pitcher has NOT pitched for BOTH the Rangers AND Seattle Mariners in their MLB career?
    a. Goose Gossage
    b. Neftalí Feliz
    c. R.A. Dickey
    d. Cliff Lee
6. How many saves did Joe Nathan record for the Rangers during the 2013 season?
    a. 37
    b. 43
    c. 46
    d. 32
7. R.A. Dickey was named to only one MLB All-Star Game in his career.
    a. True
    b. False
8. Kenny Rogers was awarded ___ Gold Gloves during his 20-season MLB career.
    a. 3
    b. 4

c. 5
d. 6

9. How many games did catcher A.J. Pierzynski play for the Rangers during the 2013 season?

    a. 101
    b. 110
    c. 121
    d. 134

10. What was Cole Hamels's win-loss record for the 2016 season with the Rangers?

    a. 15-5
    b. 12-8
    c. 13-7
    d. 14-6

11. On May 1, 1991, ______________ threw the first Rangers no-hitter at home.

    a. Kenny Rogers
    b. Nolan Ryan
    c. Bobby Witt
    d. Goose Gossage

12. Former Rangers manager Johnny Oates played for the Rangers during his MLB career as a catcher.

    a. True
    b. False

13. How many games did C.J. Wilson start for the Rangers during the 2011 season?

a. 28
b. 31
c. 33
d. 34

14. How many MLB All-Star Games was former Rangers pitcher Goose Gossage named to in his 22-season career?

    a. 3
    b. 9
    c. 10
    d. 11

15. Which MLB team did former Rangers pitcher John Wetteland NOT play for during his career?

    a. Montreal Expos
    b. Los Angeles Dodgers
    c. New York Yankees
    d. Colorado Rockies

16. Iván "Pudge" Rodriguez was charged with 127 passed balls in his career.

    a. True
    b. False

17. How many complete games did Derek Holland throw for the Rangers in 2011?

    a. 4
    b. 2
    c. 1
    d. 0

18. How many intentional walks did former Rangers pitcher Yu Darvish throw during the 2013 season?

    a. 0
    b. 1
    c. 4
    d. 5

19. How many wild pitches did Colby Lewis throw in his 2010 season with the Rangers?

    a. 0
    b. 3
    c. 6
    d. 9

20. In Scott Feldman's eight seasons spent with the Rangers, he had a winning record in only two.

    a. True
    b. False

QUIZ ANSWERS

1. C – 301
2. A – True
3. C – Cole Hamels
4. D – Jeff Banister
5. B – Neftalí Feliz
6. B – 43
7. A – True
8. C – 5
9. D – 134
10. A – 15-5
11. B – Nolan Ryan
12. B – False, He played for the Atlanta Braves, Los Angeles Dodgers, Philadelphia Phillies, New York Yankees, and Baltimore Orioles.
13. D – 34
14. B – 9
15. D – Colorado Rockies
16. A – True
17. A – 4
18. B – 1
19. D – 9
20. A – True

DID YOU KNOW?

1. Current Rangers catcher Jeff Mathis has been in the MLB for 15 seasons (as of 2019). He has also played for the Los Angeles Angels of Anaheim, the Miami Marlins, the Arizona Diamondbacks, and the Toronto Blue Jays.
2. Current Rangers pitcher Mike Minor was named to the 2019 MLB All-Star Game as a member of the Rangers.
3. Bartolo Colón pitched for the Rangers during the 2018 season at age 45. His MLB debut came in 1997 with the Cleveland Indians. He also played for the Los Angeles Angels of Anaheim, New York Mets, Oakland A's, Chicago White Sox, Minnesota Twins, Atlanta Braves, Boston Red Sox, New York Yankees, and the Montreal Expos. He is affectionately known as "Big Sexy."
4. In 11 seasons with the Texas Rangers, Bobby Witt's pitching record was exactly .500 at 104-104.
5. Hall of Fame pitcher Goose Gossage pitched for the Rangers in 1991. He also played for the Oakland A's, New York Yankees, Chicago White Sox, Pittsburgh Pirates, San Diego Padres, San Francisco Giants, Chicago Cubs, and Seattle Mariners during his 22-season career.
6. Kenny Rogers threw the only perfect game in Rangers history (as of the 2019 season).
7. Jose Canseco pitched in one game for the Rangers in 1993. He pitched one inning, gave up two hits and three earned

runs. He faced eight batters and walked three of them. His ERA was 27.00.

8. Jamie Moyer pitched two seasons for the Texas Rangers. During his 25-season MLB career, he also played for the Colorado Rockies, Seattle Mariners, Chicago Cubs, Philadelphia Phillies, Baltimore Orioles, St. Louis Cardinals, and Boston Red Sox. In those 25 years, he made the MLB All-Star Game only once.
9. During the 1987 season, Rangers pitcher Charlie Hough threw 13 complete games, started 40 games and finished 40 games, pitched 285.1 innings, and faced 1,231 batters.
10. Charlie Hough gave up the most home runs in Rangers franchise history, with 238. Second on the list is Kenny Rogers with 195 home runs given up.

CHAPTER 13:

WORLD SERIES

QUIZ TIME!

1. How many World Series have the Texas Rangers won?
    a. 0
    b. 2
    c. 4
    d. 5
2. How many AL pennants have the Texas Rangers won?
    a. 1
    b. 2
    c. 3
    d. 4
3. Which team did the Texas Rangers face in the 2010 World Series?
    a. St. Louis Cardinals
    b. Los Angeles Dodgers
    c. San Francisco Giants
    d. Washington Nationals

4. Which team did the Texas Rangers face in the 2011 World Series?
    a. St. Louis Cardinals
    b. Los Angeles Dodgers
    c. San Francisco Giants
    d. Washington Nationals
5. The Texas Rangers' only wild card berth came in _____.
    a. 2015
    b. 2014
    c. 2013
    d. 2012
6. How many games did the 2011 World Series go?
    a. 4
    b. 5
    c. 6
    d. 7
7. Nelson Cruz was named the 2011 ALCS MVP.
    a. True
    b. False
8. Who was the Texas Rangers' manager when they made the World Series in 2010 and 2011?
    a. Buck Showalter
    b. Ron Washington
    c. Jeff Banister
    d. Bobby Valentine

9. How many games did the 2010 World Series go?

   a. 4
   b. 5
   c. 6
   d. 7

10. Which pitcher started Game 1 of the 2010 World Series for the Rangers?

    a. C.J. Wilson
    b. Colby Lewis
    c. Cliff Lee
    d. Derek Holland

11. Which pitcher started Game 1 of the 2011 World Series for the Rangers?

    a. C.J. Wilson
    b. Scott Feldman
    c. Colby Lewis
    d. Derek Holland

12. Vladimir Guerrero was named the 2010 ALCS MVP.

    a. True
    b. False

13. How many American League West titles have the Texas Rangers won (as of the end of the 2019 season)?

    a. 5
    b. 6
    c. 7
    d. 9

14. Which Ranger did NOT hit a home run in the 2010 World Series?

    a. Nelson Cruz
    b. Ian Kinsler
    c. Mitch Moreland
    d. Josh Hamilton

15. Which Ranger did NOT hit a home run in the 2011 World Series?

    a. Elvis Andrus
    b. Adrián Beltré
    c. Mike Napoli
    d. Michael Young

16. The Texas Rangers won their first American League West Division Championship Title in 1995.

    a. True
    b. False

17. Which team did the Texas Rangers play in the 2012 American League Wild Card game?

    a. New York Yankees
    b. Kansas City Royals
    c. Detroit Tigers
    d. Baltimore Orioles

18. What was the final score of Game 3 of the 2010 World Series?

    a. Rangers 2, Giants 4
    b. Rangers 4, Giants 2

c. Rangers 7, Giants 11
d. Rangers 11, Giants 7

19. What was the final score of Game 4 of the 2011 World Series?

a. Rangers 4, Cardinals 0
b. Rangers 0, Cardinals 4
c. Rangers 3, Cardinals 2
d. Rangers 2, Cardinals 3

20. Which Ranger did NOT play in BOTH the 2010 AND the 2011 World Series?

a. Nelson Cruz
b. Mitch Moreland
c. Jeff Francoeur
d. Josh Hamilton

QUIZ ANSWERS

1. A – 0
2. B – 2
3. C – San Francisco Giants
4. A – St. Louis Cardinals
5. D – 2012
6. D – 7
7. A – True
8. B – Ron Washington
9. B – 5
10. C – Cliff Lee
11. A – C.J. Wilson
12. B – False, Josh Hamilton was named ALCS MVP in 2010.
13. C – 7
14. B – Ian Kinsler
15. A – Elvis Andrus
16. B – False, They won their first title in 1996.
17. D – Baltimore Orioles
18. B – Rangers 4, Giants 2
19. A – Rangers 4, Cardinals 0
20. C – Jeff Francoeur (He only played in the 2010 World Series.)

DID YOU KNOW?

1. The Texas Rangers are one of five MLB teams that have played in the World Series but have never won one. The other four teams are the San Diego Padres, the Colorado Rockies, the Tampa Bay Rays, and the Milwaukee Brewers. The Seattle Mariners, the Rangers' AL West Division foe, is the only team that has never even appeared in a World Series (as of the end of the 2019 season).

2. Of the players whose numbers have been retired by the Rangers, Nolan Ryan won one World Series with the New York Mets in 1969; Iván "Pudge" Rodriguez won one World Series with the Florida Marlins in 2003; Michael Young and Adrián Beltré never won a World Series.

3. Nelson Cruz had the most at-bats for the Rangers in the 2010 World Series, with 20. Adrián Beltré had the most at-bats for the Rangers in the 2011 World Series, with 30.

4. Neftalí Feliz recorded one save in the 2010 World Series and two saves in the 2011 World Series.

5. Mitch Moreland had the most hits for the Rangers in the 2010 World Series, with six. Adrián Beltré and Ian Kinsler tied for the most hits for the Rangers in the 2011 World Series with nine each.

6. Cliff Lee recorded the most strikeouts for the Rangers in the 2010 World Series, with 13, and C.J. Wilson led the team in the 2011 World Series, with 9.

7. The 2010 World Series began on October 27 at AT&T Park in San Francisco and ended on November 1 at Rangers Park in Arlington, Texas.
8. The 2011 World Series began on October 19 at Busch Stadium in St. Louis and ended on October 28, also at Busch Stadium.
9. Elvis Andrus, Josh Hamilton, Nelson Cruz, Ian Kinsler, Mitch Moreland, and Michael Young played in all five games of the 2010 World Series for the Rangers. Andrus, Adrián Beltré, Cruz, Hamilton, Kinsler, David Murphy, Mike Napoli, and Young played in all seven games of the 2011 World Series for the Rangers.
10. Darren O'Day pitched in the most games for the Rangers in the 2010 World Series, with four appearances, while Alexi Ogando pitched in the most games for the Rangers in the 2011 World Series, with six.

CHAPTER 14:

HEATED RIVALRIES

QUIZ TIME!

1. Which team does NOT play in the American League West with the Rangers?
   a. Oakland A's
   b. Los Angeles Dodgers
   c. Seattle Mariners
   d. Houston Astros
2. The Houston Astros and Texas Rangers have NEVER met in the MLB postseason.
   a. True
   b. False
3. When the Texas Rangers play the Houston Astros, what is the series called?
   a. Texas Series
   b. Gold Boot Series
   c. Cowboy Series
   d. Lone Star Series

4. Before the Houston Astros moved to the American League West, a trophy was given to the winner of the interleague Lone Star Series. What was the name of that trophy?
    a. The Lone Star
    b. The Silver Boot
    c. The Gold Cowboy Hat
    d. The Silver Horse
5. When was the first meeting in the Lone Star Series?
    a. June 8, 1999
    b. September 6, 2001
    c. June 8, 2001
    d. September 6, 1999
6. The Rangers have not won a World Series championship as of the end of the 2019 season. How many do the Astros have?
    a. 0
    b. 1
    c. 2
    d. 3
7. The Rangers and Houston Astros shared the Astrodome for a short period, which is a big part of their rivalry.
    a. True
    b. False
8. Which of the players below did NOT play for BOTH the Texas Rangers AND the Houston Astros?
    a. Iván Rodriguez
    b. Cliff Lee

c. C.J. Nitkowski
d. Robinson Chirinos

9. What size shoe was the Silver Boot trophy from Houston Astros' and Texas Rangers' interleague play?

    a. 12
    b. 13
    c. 14
    d. 15

10. As of the end of the 2019 season, how many meetings have occurred between the Houston Astros and Texas Rangers?

    a. 105
    b. 205
    c. 305
    d. 405

11. Current Texas Rangers manager Chris Woodward played for which American League West rival during his playing career as an infielder?

    a. Seattle Mariners
    b. Los Angeles Angels of Anaheim
    c. Houston Astros
    d. Oakland A's

12. The Texas Rangers have NEVER faced an American League West team in the playoffs.

    a. True
    b. False

13. Which of the players below did NOT play for BOTH the Texas Rangers AND the Los Angeles Angels of Anaheim?

    a. Sandy Alomar
    b. Bobby Bonds
    c. Bert Campaneris
    d. Shin-Soo Choo

14. Which of the players below did NOT play for BOTH the Texas Rangers AND the Seattle Mariners?

    a. Adrián Beltré
    b. Nelson Cruz
    c. Harold Baines
    d. Jeff Burroughs

15. Which of the players below did NOT play for BOTH the Texas Rangers AND the Oakland A's?

    a. Prince Fielder
    b. Jose Canseco
    c. Bartolo Colón
    d. Bert Campaneris

16. The Houston Astros defeated the Rangers on March 31, 2013, in their first game as a member of the American League West Division.

    a. True
    b. False

17. The San Francisco Giants defeated the Rangers in the 2010 World Series. How many World Series championships do the Giants have?

a. 3
b. 6
c. 8
d. 10

18. The St. Louis Cardinals defeated the Rangers in the 2011 World Series. How many World Series championships do the Cardinals have?

a. 9
b. 11
c. 12
d. 17

19. Nolan Ryan is the only player in MLB history to be named the DHL Hometown Hero for two teams (both the Rangers and Astros).

a. True
b. False

20. There has only been one rainout in the history of the Lone Star Series.

a. True
b. False

QUIZ ANSWERS

1. B – Los Angeles Dodgers
2. A – True
3. D – Lone Star Series
4. B – The Silver Boot
5. C – June 8, 2001
6. B – 1
7. B – False
8. B – Cliff Lee
9. D – 15
10. B – 205
11. A – Seattle Mariners
12. A – True
13. D – Shin-Soo Choo
14. C – Harold Baines
15. A – Prince Fielder
16. A – True
17. C – 8
18. B – 11
19. A – True
20. A – True

DID YOU KNOW?

1. Only one of the Rangers' no-hitters did not come against an American League West rival. Jim Bibby's in 1973 was against the Oakland A's, Bert Blyleven's in 1977 was against the California Angels, Nolan Ryan's in 1990 was against the Oakland A's, and Kenny Rogers's perfect game in 1994 was also against the California Angels. Nolan Ryan's second no-hitter with the Rangers in 1991 was against the Toronto Blue Jays.

2. The Oakland A's have the most World Series wins in the American League West, with nine. The Seattle Mariners and Texas Rangers have never won a World Series. The Los Angeles Angels of Anaheim and the Houston Astros have one World Series win each. As of the end of the 2019 season, the Oakland A's have the most American League West Division Championships, with 16. The Los Angeles Angels of Anaheim have won nine AL West Division Championships, then come the Rangers with seven, and finally the Astros with three (although they have only been in the AL West since 2013).

3. Although pitcher Nolan Ryan played for both the Texas Rangers and the Houston Astros, he chose to have his National Baseball Hall of Fame plaque adorned with a Rangers hat. Since retiring as a player, he has worked for both the Astros' and Rangers' front offices.

4. During a radio interview in 2017, Rangers manager Jeff Banister said, "All I know is they get to put Houston on their chest. We get to put Texas on ours." Astros pitcher Lance McCullers Jr. slammed him back on Twitter by saying, "It's because nobody knows what Arlington is."
5. The Rangers were the first American League West team to lose back-to-back World Series. The Oakland A's were the first American League West team to win three World Series in a row.
6. The current regular-season record in the Lone Star Series is led by the Rangers, 115-90; yet the Astros have a current win streak of seven in a row (as of the end of the 2019 season). Their last meeting at the time of this writing was September 18, 2019, when the Astros defeated the Rangers 3-2 at Minute Maid Park in Houston.
7. The Houston Astros joined the American League West in 2013. The Astros and Rangers had previously only played each other in interleague play since 2001. The move was actually to help ease the Rangers' schedule. Before the Astros joined, the Rangers were the only team in the American League West who were not on Pacific time. The Astros' joining allowed more time flexibility and gave the Rangers a closer team to play against, and it did heighten the Lone Star rivalry even more.
8. The Houston Astros won the World Series in 2017, which was the first World Series championship for a team from the state of Texas. However, this championship is

somewhat tainted because allegations came to light that the Astros used sign stealing and cheated in order to win in 2017 and beyond. The Houston Astros lost to the Washington Nationals in the 2019 World Series.

9. In 2015, the Rangers won the American League West Division and the Astros won a wild card berth. The Astros playoff slogan/campaign that season was "Come and Take It!" The Rangers taunted the Astros by claiming "We Came and Took it!" Savage.

10. Although the Astros have been in Texas for 10 more years than the Rangers, the Rangers franchise is one year older than the Astros. The Texas Rangers franchise began as the Washington Senators in 1961, and the Houston Astros franchise began as the Houston Colt .45s in 1962.

CHAPTER 15:

THE AWARDS SECTION

QUIZ TIME!

1. Who is the only Ranger ever to win a Hank Aaron Award? (He won three.)
   a. Adrián Beltré
   b. Vladimir Guerrero
   c. Alex Rodriguez
   d. Josh Hamilton
2. No Rangers manager has ever won the American League Manager of the Year Award.
   a. True
   b. False
3. Who is the only Rangers pitcher to win a Gold Glove? (He won four.)
   a. Nolan Ryan
   b. Kenny Rogers
   c. Fergie Jenkins
   d. Gaylord Perry

4. Which Ranger most recently won the AL Rookie of the Year Award (as of the end of the 2019 season)?
    a. Mike Hargrove
    b. Michael Young
    c. Jurickson Profar
    d. Neftalí Feliz
5. How many Gold Glove Awards did Iván Rodriguez win during his career with the Rangers?
    a. 10
    b. 2
    c. 6
    d. 12
6. Which Ranger won the 2010 Home Run Derby?
    a. Vladimir Guerrero
    b. Nelson Cruz
    c. Michael Young
    d. Josh Hamilton
7. No Rangers player has ever won a Cy Young Award.
    a. True
    b. False
8. Which Rangers player was named the DHL Hometown Hero? (Voted by MLB fans as the most outstanding player in franchise history.)
    a. Michael Young
    b. Nolan Ryan
    c. Iván Rodriguez
    d. Elvis Andrus

9. Which Rangers player won the 2004 All-Star Game MVP Award?

   a. Michael Young
   b. Adrián Gonzalez
   c. Alfonso Soriano
   d. Mark Teixeira

10. Who is the only Rangers player ever to win a Rawlings Platinum Gold Glove?

    a. Adrián Beltré
    b. Iván Rodriguez
    c. Ian Kinsler
    d. Mitch Moreland

11. Which Ranger won the 1974 NL MVP Award?

    a. Fergie Jenkins
    b. Mike Hargrove
    c. Dave Nelson
    d. Jeff Burroughs

12. Adrián Beltré NEVER won a Silver Slugger Award during his career with the Rangers.

    a. True
    b. False

13. Which Rangers player did NOT win an MLB Comeback Player of the Year Award?

    a. Fergie Jenkins
    b. Josh Hamilton
    c. Kevin Elster
    d. Ruben Sierra

14. What year was the Texas Rangers franchise named the Baseball America Organization of the Year?

    a. 1995
    b. 2004
    c. 2010
    d. 1989

15. How many Silver Slugger Awards did Iván Rodriguez win as a member of the Texas Rangers?

    a. 3
    b. 5
    c. 6
    d. 9

16. Only two Rangers (as of 2019 season) have ever been named the American League Rookie of the Year.

    a. True
    b. False

17. How many Gold Glove Awards did catcher Jim Sundberg win during his tenure with the Rangers?

    a. 2
    b. 4
    c. 6
    d. 9

18. Which Rangers player won the Home Run Derby in 1993?

    a. Jose Canseco
    b. Iván Rodriguez
    c. Rafael Palmeiro
    d. Juan Gonzalez

19. Two Rangers players won back-to-back Silver Slugger Awards in 2004-2005. Who were they?

    a. Mark Teixeira and Alfonso Soriano
    b. Mark Teixeira and Michael Young
    c. Alfonso Soriano and Michael Young
    d. Rod Barajas and Michael Young

20. Alex Rodriguez won the American League MVP Award in 2003.

    a. True
    b. False

QUIZ ANSWERS

1. C – Alex Rodriguez
2. B – False, Johnny Oates, Buck Showalter, Ron Washington, and Jeff Banister have won the award.
3. B – Kenny Rogers
4. D – Neftalí Feliz
5. A – 10
6. D – Josh Hamilton
7. A – True
8. B – Nolan Ryan
9. C – Alfonso Soriano
10. A – Adrián Beltré
11. D – Jeff Burroughs
12. A – True
13. B – Josh Hamilton
14. D – 1989
15. C – 6 (consecutively from 1994 through 1999)
16. A – True, Mike Hargrove (1974) and Neftalí Feliz (2010)
17. C – 6
18. D – Juan Gonzalez
19. A – Mark Teixeira and Alfonso Soriano
20. A – True

DID YOU KNOW?

1. In 1979, Jim Kern won the Rolaids Relief Man of the Year Award. Jeff Russell won the same award in 1989.
2. Mitch Moreland and Adrián Beltré both won Gold Glove Awards in 2016.
3. Rafael Palmeiro won only one Gold Glove and one Silver Slugger Award during his career with the Rangers.
4. No Rangers player has ever won a Cy Young Award. They are the only American League team that does not have a Cy Young winner.
5. Five Rangers have been named American League MVP in six different seasons: Jeff Burroughs (1974), Juan Gonzalez (1996, 1998), Iván Rodriguez (1999), Alex Rodriguez (2003), and Josh Hamilton (2010).
6. Three Rangers have won the American League batting title. They are Julio Franco (1991), Michael Young (2005), and Josh Hamilton (2010).
7. Three Rangers have led the American League in home runs during seven different seasons: Frank Howard (1968 and 1970), Juan Gonzalez (1992 and 1993), and Alex Rodriguez (2001, 2002, and 2003).
8. Four Rangers have been named the All-Star Game MVP in franchise history. They are Julio Franco (1990), Alfonso Soriano (2004), Michael Young (2006), and Josh Hamilton

(2010). This award is also known as the Ted Williams MVP Award.

9. No Rangers second baseman has ever won a Gold Glove Award.
10. The first Ranger to win a Gold Glove was Jim Sundberg in 1976.

CHAPTER 16:

THE AMERICAN DREAM CITY

QUIZ TIME!

1. At Globe Life Park, home of the Texas Rangers, the Boomstick is a 2-foot all-beef hot dog, smothered in chili, nacho cheese, jalapenos, and caramelized onions, all on top of an enormous potato bun. The whole thing weighs in at 3 pounds. How much does the Boomstick cost (as of 2019)?

    a. $15
    b. $22
    c. $26
    d. $32

2. Both the dot race and ballpark nachos were created at Arlington Stadium, former home of the Texas Rangers.

    a. True
    b. False

3. Known as "Vegas before Vegas," what was the name of the secret hub for gambling in Arlington during the 1920s and 1930s?

a. Top O′ Mountain Terrace
b. Top O′ World Terrace
c. Top O′ Hill Terrace
d. Top O′ Tree Terrace

4. Which car company opened an assembly plant in Arlington in 1954?

a. Volkswagen
b. Chevrolet
c. Ford
d. General Motors

5. The founder of which shoe brand was born and raised in Arlington?

a. Converse
b. TOMS
c. Vans
d. Birkenstock

6. Arlington is home to over 380,000 people, making it the _____ largest city in the United States by population.

a. 30th
b. 40th
c. 50th
d. 60th

7. Arlington is the headquarters of American Mensa.

a. True
b. False

8. What is the name of the NFL team that currently calls Arlington home?

   a. Dallas Dodgers
   b. Dallas Cowboys
   c. Dallas Raiders
   d. Dallas Mavericks

9. What is the name of the NBA team closest to Arlington?

   a. Dallas Cowboys
   b. Dallas Knicks
   c. Dallas Warriors
   d. Dallas Mavericks

10. In what year was the City of Arlington founded?

    a. 1866
    b. 1876
    c. 1886
    d. 1896

11. Arlington is home to Six Flags over Texas AND Six Flags ____________________.

    a. Hurricane Harbor
    b. Water World
    c. Discovery Kingdom
    d. Magic Mountain

12. The International Bowling Museum and Hall of Fame is located in Arlington.

    a. True
    b. False

13. The City of Arlington was named after General Robert E. Lee's hometown in __________.

    a. Indiana
    b. North Dakota
    c. Virginia
    d. Louisiana

14. Which of the following was invented in Arlington?

    a. Dental floss
    b. Microscope
    c. Washing machine
    d. Frozen margarita machine

15. How many public parks is Arlington home to?

    a. 55
    b. 67
    c. 82
    d. 99

16. The Dallas Cowboys' stadium is home to the world's largest HD TV screen at 2,100 feet across.

    a. True
    b. False

17. What county is Arlington located in?

    a. Dallas County
    b. Tarrant County
    c. Swisher County
    d. Tyler County

18. Arlington is located a little over 10 miles from the Dallas/Fort Worth International Airport. What is Dallas/Fort Worth International Airport's code?

    a. FWT
    b. DFT
    c. DTX
    d. DFW

19. What is the name of the WNBA team based in Arlington?

    a. Dallas Mavericks
    b. Dallas Mystics
    c. Dallas Wings
    d. Dallas Fever

20. Arlington is the largest city in the world that does not have a fixed public transportation system.

    a. True
    b. False

QUIZ ANSWERS

1. C – $26
2. A – True
3. C – Top O' Hill Terrace
4. D – General Motors
5. B – TOMS
6. C – 50th
7. A – True
8. B – Dallas Cowboys
9. D – Dallas Mavericks
10. B – 1876
11. A – Hurricane Harbor
12. A – True
13. C – Virginia
14. D – Frozen margarita machine
15. C – 82
16. A – True
17. B – Tarrant County
18. D – DFW
19. C – Dallas Wings
20. A – True

DID YOU KNOW?

1. Within a 12-month time frame, the City of Arlington hosted NFL Super Bowl XLV, an NBA All-Star Game, and an MLB World Series.
2. The original Six Flags theme park opened in Arlington in August 1961. Six Flags over Texas was the first regional theme park in America.
3. The Arlington Archosaur Site has uncovered 2,000 individual dinosaur fossils since 2008, and excavation continues to this day.
4. The Texas Skyscreamer at Six Flags over Texas holds the Guinness World Record for the "world's tallest swing carousel ride."
5. Arlington is set to be the home of the National Medal of Honor Museum. Construction is estimated to cost $150 million and is aimed to be completed in 2024.
6. The most popular college in Arlington is the University of Texas at Arlington. Go Mavericks!
7. Texas Live! opened in 2018. It is home to shopping, dining, a hotel, and even a convention center. It is located directly outside of the Rangers' new ballpark.
8. MLB players Vernon Wells, Ben Grieve, Hunter Pence, and John Lackey all grew up in Arlington and/or attended college there.

9. The top 10 employers in Arlington are Arlington Independent School District, the University of Texas at Arlington, General Motors, Texas Health Resources, Six Flags over Texas, The Parks at Arlington, GM Financial, the City of Arlington, JP Morgan Chase, and the Texas Rangers Baseball Club.
10. AT&T Stadium in Arlington, home of the Dallas Cowboys, cost $1.48 billion to construct.

CHAPTER 17:

YOUNG AT HEART

QUIZ TIME!

1. Where was Michael Young born?
    a. Pomona, California
    b. Covina, California
    c. Anaheim, California
    d. Temecula, California
2. Michael Young is currently special assistant to the GM for the Rangers.
    a. True
    b. False
3. Michael Young played for three teams during his MLB playing career. Which team did he NOT play for?
    a. Seattle Mariners
    b. Texas Rangers
    c. Los Angeles Dodgers
    d. Philadelphia Phillies

4. What year was Michael Young born?
    a. 1971
    b. 1973
    c. 1975
    d. 1976
5. What year was Michael Young's number 10 retired by the Texas Rangers?
    a. 2016
    b. 2017
    c. 2019
    d. They have not yet retired his number.
6. In the 25th round of the 1994 MLB Draft, Michael Young was drafted by the ____________ but did not sign. Michael Young was again drafted in the 5th round of the 1997 MLB Draft by the ______________.
    a. Baltimore Orioles, Toronto Blue Jays
    b. Toronto Blue Jays, Baltimore Orioles
    c. Texas Rangers, Toronto Blue Jays
    d. Toronto Blue Jays, Texas Rangers
7. Michael Young is in the National Baseball Hall of Fame.
    a. True
    b. False
8. Where did Michael Young attend college?
    a. University of California - Irvine
    b. San Diego State University
    c. Pepperdine University
    d. University of California - Santa Barbara

9. Where did Michael Young attend high school?

   a. Bishop Amat Memorial High School
   b. San Gabriel High School
   c. Gabrielino High School
   d. South El Monte High School

10. Michael Young launched his own charity in 2011. Its mission is to be "a charity which supports the involvement of children's health in all areas: physical, social, mental, and educational." What is the name of his charity?

    a. The Michael Young Foundation
    b. Young Foundation
    c. Michael Young Family Foundation
    d. Young Family Foundation

11. Michael Young won the Marvin Miller Man of the Year Award in ________ and ________. The Marvin Miller Man of the Year Award is given annually to the MLB player "whose on-field performance and contributions to his community inspire others to higher levels of achievement." He is one of only four players who won the award multiple times. Others on the list are John Smoltz, Jim Thome, and Curtis Granderson.

    a. 2008, 2010
    b. 2008, 2011
    c. 2010, 2012
    d. 2010, 2011

12. Michael Young is a cousin of former WBO Boxing Champion, Zack Padilla.

a. True
b. False

13. What year was Michael Young inducted into the Texas Rangers Hall of Fame?

a. 2014
b. 2015
c. 2016
d. 2019

14. What is Michael Young's full name?

a. Michael Brian Young
b. Brian Michael Young
c. Michael Brendon Young
d. Brendon Michael Young

15. What year did Michael Young's playing career end?

a. 2012
b. 2013
c. 2014
d. 2015

16. Michael Young had five consecutive 200-hit seasons.

a. True
b. False

17. What year did Michael Young make his MLB debut with the Rangers?

a. 1999
b. 2000

c. 2001
d. 2003

18. How many MLB All-Star Games was Michael Young named to during his career?

a. 5
b. 6
c. 7
d. 8

19. How many Gold Glove Awards did Michael Young win during his career?

a. 0
b. 1
c. 3
d. 9

20. Michael Young was the 2005 American League batting champion.

a. True
b. False

QUIZ ANSWERS

1. B – Covina, California
2. A – True
3. A – Seattle Mariners
4. D – 1976
5. C – 2019
6. A – Baltimore Orioles, Toronto Blue Jays
7. B – False
8. D – University of California - Santa Barbara
9. A – Bishop Amat Memorial High School
10. C – Michael Young Family Foundation
11. B – 2008, 2011
12. A – True
13. C – 2016
14. A – Michael Brian Young
15. B – 2013
16. A – True
17. B – 2000
18. C – 7
19. B – 1
20. A – True

DID YOU KNOW?

1. "Michael was one of the greatest teammates I've ever had. A competitor at heart but also a superb leader and the kind of person you want your children to look up to as a role model. He was a defining part of my time in Texas and I join all his fans in saluting his career on and off the field." – Alex Rodriguez
2. Michael Young married his high school sweetheart, Cristina. Cristina is of Mexican-American descent, and so is Michael's mother. The two have three sons together: Mateo, Emilio, and Antonio.
3. Michael Young's post-baseball hobbies include golfing and billiards.
4. Michael Young played in the longest All-Star Game in MLB history. He drove in the winning run in the 2008 MLB All-Star Game after more than four-and-a-half hours of playing time.
5. Michael Young was eligible for the National Baseball Hall of Fame in 2019. However, he only won 2.1% of the vote, which makes him ineligible from here on out.
6. After making it to the Majors, Michael Young donated money to refurbish UC Santa Barbara's baseball field.
7. Don Mattingly was Michael Young's favorite player when he was growing up. He got to play for Don Mattingly

when he was with the Dodgers in 2013, when Mattingly was their manager.

8. Michael Young was named the 2006 MLB All-Star Game MVP at PNC Park in Pittsburgh.
9. Michael Young hit 185 home runs in his 14-season career.
10. Michael Young's career batting average was a crisp .300.

CHAPTER 18:

PUDGE

QUIZ TIME!

1. Where was Iván Rodriguez born?
    a. San Juan, Puerto Rico
    b. Manatí, Puerto Rico
    c. Santo Domingo, Dominican Republic
    d. Havana, Cuba
2. Iván Rodriguez often played against former Ranger Juan Gonzalez during his youth.
    a. True
    b. False
3. What year was Iván Rodriguez elected to the National Baseball Hall of Fame?
    a. 2015
    b. 2016
    c. 2017
    d. 2018

4. When was Iván Rodriguez born?

    a. April 30, 1971
    b. April 30, 1969
    c. November 27, 1969
    d. November 27, 1971

5. Iván Rodriguez played for six MLB teams in his 21-season career. Which team did Pudge NOT play for?

    a. Washington Nationals
    b. San Diego Padres
    c. Detroit Tigers
    d. Florida Marlins

6. How old was Iván Rodriguez when he signed with the Texas Rangers?

    a. 16
    b. 18
    c. 21
    d. 24

7. After announcing his retirement, Iván Rodriguez signed a one-day contract with the Rangers so he could retire as a member of the team.

    a. True
    b. False

8. What is the name of Iván Rodriguez's autobiography?

    a. *They Call Me Pudge: Behind the Plate for the Rangers*
    b. *Pudge: My Career Behind the Plate*
    c. *They Call Me Pudge: My Life Playing the Game I Love*
    d. *Iván Rodriguez: My Life Playing the Game I Love*

9. What year did the Texas Rangers retire Iván Rodriguez's number 7?

   a. 2015
   b. 2016
   c. 2017
   d. 2018

10. What year was Iván Rodriguez named American League MVP?

    a. 1998
    b. 1999
    c. 2000
    d. 2001

11. How many MLB All-Star Games was Iván Rodriguez named to?

    a. 12
    b. 16
    c. 2
    d. 14

12. In his book *Juiced,* Jose Canseco claimed he personally injected Iván Rodriguez with steroids.

    a. True
    b. False

13. Iván Rodriguez won one World Series with the ________________.

    a. Florida Marlins
    b. Houston Astros

c. Detroit Tigers
d. New York Yankees

14. Who gave Iván Rodriguez the nickname "Pudge"?

a. Bobby Valentine
b. Tom Grieve
c. George W. Bush
d. Chino Cadahia

15. What year was Iván Rodriguez named to the Texas Sports Hall of Fame?

a. 2013
b. 2014
c. 2015
d. 2017

16. Iván Rodriguez NEVER won a Gold Glove Award.

a. True
b. False

17. How many Silver Slugger Awards did Iván Rodriguez win during his career?

a. 4
b. 5
c. 6
d. 7

18. Where did Iván Rodriguez attend high school?

a. Escuela Superior Lino Padron Rivera
b. Emilio R. Delgado High School

c. Carlos Gonzalez High School
d. Escuela Superior Juan Quirindongo Morell

19. Iván Rodriguez's son, Iván Dereck, was drafted in the 6th round of the 2011 MLB Draft as a pitcher by the ____________________.

a. Texas Rangers
b. Minnesota Twins
c. Houston Astros
d. New York Mets

20. Iván Rodriguez caught 2,427 games, the most of any catcher in the history of Major League Baseball.

a. True
b. False

QUIZ ANSWERS

1. B – Manatí, Puerto Rico
2. A – True
3. C – 2017
4. D – November 27, 1971
5. B – San Diego Padres
6. A – 16
7. A – True
8. C – *They Call Me Pudge: My Life Playing the Game I Love*
9. C – 2017
10. B – 1999
11. D – 14
12. A – True
13. A – Florida Marlins
14. D – Chino Cadahia
15. B – 2014
16. B – False, He won 13.
17. D – 7
18. A – Escuela Superior Lino Padron Rivera
19. B – Minnesota Twins
20. A – True

DID YOU KNOW?

1. Iván Rodriguez starred in a Texas government PSA about safety protocols during the COVID-19 pandemic. He said, "My whole entire career I've been using this mask. Now I want to ask you to wear your mask to keep our businesses safe for you."
2. Iván Rodriguez joined Fox Sports Southwest in 2014 as a pre- and post-game analyst.
3. Iván Rodriguez was called up to the big leagues the same day that he got married to his first wife.
4. Iván founded the Iván "Pudge" Rodriguez Foundation, which helps families of children who have cancer. He is also a partner of the Make-a-Wish Foundation.
5. Iván Rodriguez played for Team Puerto Rico in the 2006 and 2009 World Baseball Classic. He was also named to the All-World Baseball Classic team.
6. Pudge was inducted into the National Baseball Hall of Fame in his first year of eligibility with 76% of the vote.
7. Iván Rodriguez's first job was passing out flyers in shopping malls in Puerto Rico.
8. When he was growing up, Iván Rodriguez's favorite baseball player was fellow catcher Johnny Bench.
9. Iván Rodriguez caught Kenny Rogers's perfect game on July 28, 1994.

10. Iván Rodriguez was named the NLCS MVP in 2003, when he was with the Florida Marlins. He went on to win his only World Series with the Marlins. He played in the 2006 World Series with the Detroit Tigers, but the St. Louis Cardinals won.

CONCLUSION

Learn anything new? Now you truly are the ultimate Rangers fan. Not only did you learn about the Rangers of the modern era, but you also expanded your knowledge back to the Washington Senators days.

You learned about the Rangers' origins and their history. You learned about the history of their uniforms and jersey numbers. You identified some famous quotes and read some of the craziest nicknames of all time. You learned more about the famous Nolan Ryan, who is widely regarded as one of the best pitchers of all time. I mean, not every pitcher throws seven no-hitters in their career—he was impressive, to say the very least. You learned more about the legendary Iván "Pudge" Rodriguez and the Rangers' constant for so many years, Michael Young. You were exposed to some Rangers stats and recalled some of the best-known Rangers trades and draft picks of all time. Knowledge was broken down by outfielders, infielders, pitchers, and catchers. You looked back on the Rangers' playoff feats and the awards that came before, after, and during them. You also learned about the Rangers' fiercest rivalries of all time, including the Houston Astros, Oakland A's, Seattle Mariners, and the Los Angeles Angels of Anaheim.

Every team in the MLB has a storied history, but the Rangers have one of the most interesting of all. They have never won a World Series, which takes some dedicated fans. Being the ultimate Rangers fan takes a lot of knowledge and patience, which you tested with this book. Whether you knew every answer or were stumped by several questions, you learned some of the most incredible history that the game of baseball has to offer.

The history of the Rangers represents what we all love about the game of baseball. The heart, the determination, the tough times, and the unexpected moments, plus the players that inspire us and encourage us to do our best, because even if you get knocked down, there is always another game and another day.

With players like Elvis Andrus, Rougned Odor, and Joey Gallo, the future for the Rangers looks bright. There is no doubt that this franchise will continue to be one of the most competitive sports teams in Major League Baseball every year.

It's a new decade, and the Rangers have a new ballpark to call home, which means there is a clean slate, ready to continue writing the history of the Texas Rangers. The ultimate Rangers fans cannot wait to see what's to come for their Lone Stars.

Made in the USA
Coppell, TX
23 December 2021